MEDICINE AND MYTH

THE BIBLE:
MEDICINE AND MYTH

MARGARET LLOYD DAVIES
BA BD STh

T.A. LLOYD DAVIES
MD FRCP

SILENT BOOKS

CAMBRIDGE

ACKNOWLEDGEMENTS

Professor Richard Schilling CBE, MD, FRCP, has given much encouragement and Mr Michael Gracey MA, has provided valuable historical and linguistic support. In addition we thank Mr Eric Kent MA, for reading and commenting on the text. Miss Emma Sayers BSc, kindly undertook the calculation in Table 5.

We are grateful for permission to reproduce the following: Figure 2 from Oxford Scientific Films, Figure 3 from Sir Cyril Clark, Figures 4 & 5 from Dr Ralph Muller, photograph by Ahmed Tayeh, Figure 6 from Bruce Coleman Limited and Figure 8 from The Bridgeman Art Library Ltd.

Mr David Hodgkiss designed the cover.

Note

1. All biblical references (Old Testament, New Testament and Apocryphal) are to the Revised Standard Version of the Bible (RSV).
2. Within chapters covering an individual book of the Bible, the title of the book is not repeated in the biblical references.

Second edition published in Great Britain 1993
by Silent Books, Swavesey, Cambridge CB4 5RA

First published in Great Britain 1991
by Allborough Publishing, Cambridge

ISBN 1 85183 053 7

British Library Cataloguing-in-Publication Data.
A catalogue record for this book is available from the British Library.

Typeset by Action Typesetting Ltd
Printed in Great Britain by
Tabro Litho, Ramsey, Cambridgeshire

CONTENTS

INTRODUCTION

The aim of this book is to apply modern medical knowledge to incidents in the Bible. The biblical narratives are considered in the order in which they occur in the Bible and the text used is that of the Revised Standard Version. No attempt is made to analyse the historicity of events and stories. Where matters of medical interest arise account has been taken of material from other sources. Where the books or the narrative have no medical cognition, they are omitted.

The events described in the Bible affected real persons whose hopes and disappointments, successes and failures differ only from those of people living today by being expressed in another culture. All incidents in the Bible affecting human beings are capable of being explained by normal and natural processes of the body or mind. This means that the traditional interpretations of some of the events in the Bible, notably the Virgin Birth and the Resurrection, cannot be supported unless the integrity of medical diagnosis is sacrificed. Of course, retrospective diagnosis may be erroneous, but the application of newer knowledge may provide a starting point for a developing Christianity.

All men like to find reasons for their experiences; invocation of the supernatural was necessary in the past because of insufficient knowledge. The Christian faith is burdened with imagery inherited from its earliest days; indeed much of it came from the Apostles' need to explain phenomena beyond their comprehension. The Early Fathers argued logically within the bounds of their knowledge; the supernatural was not introduced until this boundary was reached. Theological beliefs as enshrined in the creeds are fixed by modes of thought of the fourth century or earlier. This is no longer necessary because of advances in biblical scholarship nor is it acceptable to scientifically sophisticated populations. No longer are miracles credible explanations of events observed long ago. Unless faith is to be destroyed by myth, supernatural assertions must give way to modern knowledge. This book is not an attack on Christianity but an attempt to explain the Bible.

Theology has accepted physical and scientific advances in knowledge, but is hesitant about medical science. Affirmations of belief interpreted by colourful ceremonies appealing to the emotions, essential though these were in earlier ages, are no longer sufficient. Only 12 per cent of the population, mostly elderly, attend church regularly. The young want more than a periodic topping-up of beliefs. They want a church where they can find a meaning to life not repugnant to science. The mind works as a whole, in future the intellect as well as the emotions must be engaged. Endeavours to perpetuate the intellectuallyincredible will bring decay no matter what the institution. It would be tragic if this happened to the church, as the Christian faith has so much to offer, both to the individual and to the community. Faith does not require the abandonment of intellectual enquiry or the assent to concepts not scientifically acceptable. Jesus commanded his disciples to love the Lord their God with all their heart, with all their soul and with all their *mind*. The church will be stronger if it accommodates proven knowledge within its creeds, though the jump from certainty to the doubt of thinking is frightening. If the church ignores modern knowledge all that is left is blind belief, far beyond the credulity of most people. Belief in the supernatural is not necessary for belief in Christ. Indeed, without the supernatural he is the greater. Jesus Christ is the most significant person in history. He does not need myth to live on 'far away, woven into the stuff of other men's lives'.

Margaret Lloyd Davies
T.A. Lloyd Davies
Elmdon
Saffron Walden CB11 4NL
February 1993

IMPORTANT DATES

Middle Bronze Age		
c. 2000–1550BC	c. 1570BC	Abraham left Haran with his family and flocks and emigrated to Palestine
Late Bronze Age		
c. 1550–1200 BC	c. 1500–1300	Hebrews in Egypt
	c. 1280–1250	Exodus from Egypt
	c. 1250–1200	Israelite conquest of Canaan
Iron Age		
1200–332BC	c. 1200–1020	The period of the Judges
	c. 1020–1000	Saul
	c. 1000–961	David
	c. 961–922	Solomon
	922	The Division of the Kingdom
		For the Kings of the divided Kingdom see Table 4 on page 140
	722	Fall of Samaria (Israel)
	587	Fall of Jerusalem (Judah)
	587–538	Exile in Babylon
		Written and oral sources comprising the Pentateuch (the first five books of the Bible) were edited into their final form during or just after the Exile
	538	Edict of Cyrus. Return from Exile
	520–515	Rebuilding of Temple
	444–398	Work of Nehemiah and Ezra
Hellenistic Period		
332–63BC		Palestine ruled by Ptolemies and Seleucids
	c. 250	Old Testament translated into Greek in Alexandria, version known as Septuagint
	167	Start of Maccabean rebellion
		Book of Daniel
Roman Period		
63BC–AD324	63	Roman conquest of Palestine
	4BC–AD39	Herod Antipas Tetrarch of Galilee
	26	Pontius Pilate appointed Prefect of Judaea
	c. 30/33	Jesus's Crucifixion
	c. 35	Stephen martyred
	c. 37	Paul's journey to Damascus
	c. 48	Paul's letter to the Galatians
	49	Council of Jerusalem
	c. 50	Paul's letters to Thessalonians
	c. 54	Paul's first letter to Corinthians
		Paul's letter to Philippians
	c. 55	Paul's second letter to Corinthians
	c. 57	Paul's letter to Romans
	c. 58–60	Paul's journey to Rome
	c. 60	Paul's letters to Colossians, Philemon and possibly Ephesians written from Rome
	64	Neronian persecution. Peter and Paul's execution in Rome.
	c. 65–70	Gospel of Mark written in Rome
	66–70	Jewish Rebellion against Rome
	70	Capture of Jerusalem by Titus
	c. 70–80	Gospels of Matthew and Luke
	c. 80	Acts of the Apostles
	c. 90–100	Gospel of John
	325	Council of Nicaea which formulated the Nicene Creed

1

GENESIS

God made the world and 'God saw that it was good' (1:18). He gave man dominion over all that was in it (1:26), which as things have turned out, if a mere mortal may say so, was a mistake (*see Figures 1 and 2*). The world has become an unjust world, both between different species (especially mankind and animals) and between men, women and children living in different parts of it.

POSITION OF WOMEN

The tedious tribal genealogy obscures the lack of regard paid to women. The subjugation of women is the oustanding impression of any fair reading of Genesis; feminists would do well to remember what Christ did for women. Little more than breeding machines, their function was to people the land or at least that part of the land occupied by their husbands' tribes. 'God created man in his own image . . . ; male and female he created them' (1:27). 'Be fruitful and multiply' (1:28). 'I [God] will greatly multiply your pain in childbearing . . . yet your desire shall be for your husband, and he shall rule over you' (3:16). Lengthy lists of names (all male) of children begotten by various men suggest that these exhortations were obeyed with alacrity. The superiority of the male was emphasised (Exodus 21:7).

1

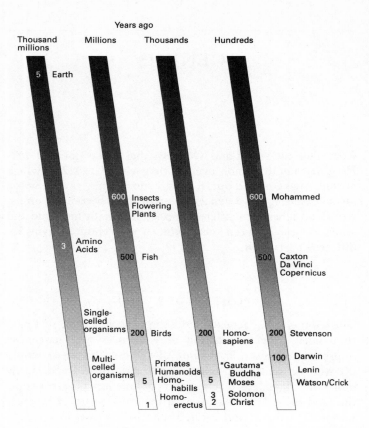

Figure 1   The Puniness of Man
The earth consolidated between 5 and 15 thousand million years ago. Life originated 3–4 thousand million years ago in outer space. The estimate of the number of species which have appeared is 4.5 million, each with an approximate life of 2.7 million years before becoming extinct. The sun is expected to die out in 5 thousand million years.

Figure 2   Orang-utan (Man-monkey)
In danger of extinction because of the destruction of their habitat in Indonesia.

Some men did not even choose their wives for themselves but a servant was sent to make a choice. Abraham sent a servant who, following the practice of the Semites (who believed the loin or thigh was the seat of life[1]), gave an oath by placing his hand on Abraham's thigh before departing to select a wife for Isaac. Though asked whether she wished to leave her family, Rebekah accepted her fate meekly. Despite this arranged marriage, Isaac is reported as loving Rebekah (24:67), though a later incident suggests that his own skin was more important. No doubt the better-looking women were chosen first and by the sons of the more important families.

PHYSIQUE AND MARRIAGE

Among women attending the Aberdeen Maternity Hospital in the 1950s taller women tended to marry upwards in social class (comparing the occupations of their husbands and fathers classified by the Registrar-General). In Britain, height is an important component of beauty: tall women (over 64 inches, 162.6 cm in height) observed by Baird[2,3] in Aberdeen had either husbands or fathers whose occupation was classified in Social Class I or II by the Registrar-General or who themselves had a similarly classified occupation before marriage. Even if tall women lived in a more favourable environment than short women (height less than 61 inches, 154.9 cm) hereditary factors, not fully understood, played a part in making tall women more efficient mothers. For example, the premature birth rate varied from 3.8 per hundred for tall mothers to 14.3 per hundred for short mothers and the perinatal rate (deaths of infants in first week of life and still births) from 14.5 to 55 per thousand births. Baird[2] has suggested that the relative distribution of tall and short women in a community would be a simple but effective measure of the health of women.

Similar observations in 1985[4] showed that, while there had been across-the-board improvement in the health of mothers and babies in Aberdeen, the relative differences between social classes remained. Marriage customs had changed, stable unions outside marriage were common, the mother's occupation provided greater discrimination than the father's and female birth control changed conception from fatalistic acceptance to planned parenthood.

The Song of Solomon describes the desirable qualities in a woman very much as prized in Western cultures today – scarlet lips, fragrant kisses, dark hair, shining eyes, smooth neck and nice thighs, but height is implied only by the need to be swift.

Even though more boys than girls were born (a ratio of about 1.05 to 1.00) there were plenty of women in the patriarchal society. The survival rate of boys in infancy is lower so that the ratio is reversed. To this must be added the wastage of men in wars, by fighting and by injury. In Britain, sophisticated public services (including housing and nutrition) combined with a superb National Health Service mean that more boys are surviving to outnumber girls at marriageable age.

RISKS OF CHILDBEARING

Childbearing was a deathly gamble fraught with misery for those who survived. Today, pregnancy and childbirth kill 1 in 21 women in Africa, 1 in 54 in Asia and 1 in 73 in Latin America. The early Hebrew women were unlikely to have fared better. Uterine prolapse of every degree, incontinence and vesico-vaginal fistula would be fairly common among those women who survived toxaemia, haemorrhage, sepsis and obstructed labour. Pregnant teenage girls would be at greatest risk. Women were not helped by dietary limitations which must already have been creeping in, although not yet codified (Deuteronomy 14:3 – 21), or by the fact that they ate after their husbands and children i.e. they lived on leftovers. The first labour would be the most difficult and painful (Jeremiah 4:31). Antenatal classes would be unknown and old wives' gossip undoubtedly frightened many girls.

Comparison of the gynaecological condition of women of 13 years or over in two Indian rural villages surveyed by Bang et al.[5] with that of women living c.2000–1300 BC, the time span from the patriarchs to the end of Genesis, may be unfair, but Israelite women of that period are unlikely to have fared better. The Indian survey involved matters of great sensitivity, especially in Hindu society, but 650 women or 59 per hundred of those eligible responded. Ninety-two (14 per hundred) were unmarried and of those ever married 58 per hundred had a bad obstetric history. The mean parity (number of pregnancies) was 3.99. Only two women had gonorrhoea, which is a very favourable comparison with the implications of Leviticus and Deuteronomy; 599 (92.2 per hundred) women had one or more gynaecological or sexual disease; the average number of diseases present was 3.6. Among the unmarried girls 47 per hundred had experienced sexual intercourse. Nearly all the women (91 per hundred) suffered from anaemia, including 83 per hundred due to iron deficiency; 12 per hundred suffered from pulmonary tuberculosis.

The survey by Bang et al.[5] was of survivors. We have no means of estimating the deaths consequent upon childbirth among Israelite women. Recent studies have shown that pregnancy-related deaths are 24 per year for 1000 women of childbearing age in isolated Gambian villages, a situation which might be likened to the sixteenth to eighteenth centuries in England. Today in Egypt 19 per hundred of all female deaths are maternally related. The maternal mortality rate[*]

---

[*]Deaths due to complications in pregnancy, childbirth and puerperium per thousand live and still births.

in England and Wales has been reduced from 4.1 in 1931 to 0.07 in 1985. The estimated rate for the whole world is 3.5; in India it is 6.0. The most recent rate (1984) for Burma is 50.0.

More noteworthy is an observation by Briggs and Oruamabo[6] from Nigeria that, in the years 1987, 1988 and 1989, the literacy of the mother greatly influenced perinatal mortality. For 'unbooked' deliveries the maternal mortality for literate mothers was 5.2 per thousand and for illiterate mothers 15.1 per thousand. For 'booked' deliveries, the corresponding figures were 1.3 and 6.4.

ADAM AND EVE

Deep sleep was sufficient anaesthetic for Adam's resection of rib (2:21), but to suppose that Eve might be cloned from Adam's rib is to turn the evolutionary process upside down. If the biblical account is to be believed, Adam cannot have had a mother. Field[7] suggests that the story of Adam and Eve derived from the tale of a solitary settler, Adam, who was permitted to farm a very fertile piece of land, the Garden of Eden, near the Euphrates. A slave girl, Eve, was given to him by the owner. The landlord reserved a sacred tree to himself, hence the expulsion after Eve ate the fruit bringing the biblical punishment of pain in childbirth on her gender.

Before creationists tilt at the facts of evolution they should resolve the differences between the two stories of creation (1:27 and 2:7, 22). Analysis of the DNA of the mitochrondia (small organelles in which most metabolic processes are undertaken) found lying in the cytoplasm of the human cells proves that they are derived from the ovum. If Eve, as the creationists maintain, was the sole ancestress of the human race, she lived in Africa, in the Neanderthal period about 200,000 years ago and had a darkly pigmented skin. Indeed, polygyny makes it probable that many male lineages became extinct and that 'Eve' predated Adam. If this is true, as seems likely, evolutionary 'Eve' was more than one woman.[8]

The Lord does not appear to have been understanding. As a good husband Adam would have listened to his wife (3:17). The worst sexist retribution inflicted by the Lord was to introduce sexual shame and prudery (3:7).

WATER

The early Israelite (and pre-Israelite) society was onerous, the environment was harsh, scraping a living out of a water-starved desert. As the Exodus proved, water is essential to life, both to man and his animals. Wells were extremely important (26:18). No doubt each family would defend its well vigorously (13:7, 11). Abraham's servant, sent to find a wife for Isaac, found Rebekah by a well drawing water. Jacob met and kissed Rachel at a well (29:11). Moses's quick indignation in defending Reu'el's (Jethro's) daughters against interfering shepherds whilst watering their sheep (Exodus 2:17) resulted in his marriage to Zipporah. Except for springs and artesian wells, such as the water that poured through a line of cleavage when Moses struck a rock at Horeb (Exodus 17:6), the only method of drawing water would be by rope and bucket. Spillage from the bucket would fall on the ground and in the absence of an impermeable surround would seep back into the well and be a very likely source of contamination. The head of the well was protected by a large stone. Later, after the conquest of Canaan, the Israelites copied the Canaanites and stored water in cisterns carved out of the rock such as those to be seen near Masada.

ABRAHAM'S DECEIT

The worst humiliation of women is the story, recorded three times in Genesis, – when a man, in order to save his own life, said that his wife was his sister and therefore was available to other men. Abram,* when he was in Egypt to escape the famine, told Pharaoh that his wife, Sarai,† was his sister (12:13); she was in fact his half-sister (20:12). Pharaoh took Sarai to his house, had intercourse with her and as a result Pharaoh and Egypt were afflicted with 'plagues'. In the absence of any description nothing can be said about the cause of these plagues except to speculate that infectious diseases must have been widespread in Egypt. Abram may have saved his own life and Pharaoh would have taken Sarai anyway. His action may have been sensible or even proper in a bellicose age. Later, Abraham told Abimelech, King of Gerar, that Sarah was his sister (20:2), but Abimelech learnt the truth in a dream and, not surprisingly, was angry with Abraham because if he had had intercourse with Sarah he would have been a partner in adultery. Isaac followed the family tradition and described Rebekah as his sister (26:7), again to ensure his own safety; but this time Abimelech saw through the deception (26:9).

SEXUAL PROWESS

Claims of sexual prowess were frequent. Adam became a father at the reputed age of 130 years (5:3), Seth at 105 (5:6), Enoch at 65 (5:21) and Noah became the father of Shem, Ham and Japheth after the age of 500 years (5:32) (see page 20). Sarah gave birth to Isaac, Abraham's son, after the menopause (18:11, 21:2), not impossible but extremely unlikely and certainly not possible at the age of 90 years (17:18), especially as Abraham was 100 years old! It is interesting, as so often with adoptions, that Sarah conceived after the birth of Abraham's son by Hagar. If the story of Adam and Eve is to be believed, Cain's wife, the mother of Enoch (4:17), was his sister.

---

*His name was subsequently changed to Abraham (17:5).
†Her name was subsequently changed to Sarah (17:15).

AGE OF MENARCHE AND CONCEPTION

Girls among primitive people are subject to indefatigable intercourse from an early age. The age of menarche in Western countries, including Britain, has been getting earlier since nutrition improved and, though having a wide age spread, 10 to 11 years is now common. The age of menarche, though with a wide spread among girls of the early Israelite society, is likely to have been later, not earlier, possibly as late as 18 years, which was common in Victorian England. If girls in early Israelite society were fortunate, adolescent sterility (which protects immature females during the period in which they are physically suited to intercourse but not able to bear the stress of reproduction) preserved them from the dangers of childbirth until they were older. Montague[9] demonstrated adolescent sterility in animals. Some support for this is given by Duncan's[10] observation in the last century that in Scots girls marrying between 15 and 19 years of age and in American and Chinese girls (who almost certainly did not use contraception) pregnancy was rare before 20 years of age.

Among the Murats of Borneo, infection with an anaerobic *Streptococcus* caused obstruction of the Fallopian tubes and hence sterility. Depopulation was the consequence.[11,12] One theory of how the infection was introduced is that the wearing of shorts by boys allowed the penis to harbour infection. Such is most unlikely to have been the fate of pre-Israelite girls as shorts were unknown, but it is worth considering whether infection of whatever sort limited the number of children borne by women. There is evidence that gonorrhoea existed (Leviticus 15:2), though it is not mentioned in Genesis.

CHILDREN

The advantages of having children were enormous, both in the hereafter and in this world. The early Israelites believed not so much in personal survival but that they lived on in their children. Destiny was in their name. The mortality among the new born and children would have been enormous; particularly in the first year of life (see page 6). A recent paper[13] surveying rural villages in India shows that without intervention by health personnel, only 787 children in every 1000 born survived one year after birth. This made the need for children more demanding. Michal, the wife of David and daughter of Saul, was held in contempt because she 'had no child to the day of her death' (II Samuel 6:23) (see page 123).

The need for children no doubt accounted for surrogacy: for example, Abraham and Hagar (16:3), Jacob and Bilhah (30:3) and Jacob and Zilpah (30:9). Abraham and his wife Sarah did not have any children (16:1), but Sarah, acknowledging that Abraham lived on in his children, suggested that he should have intercourse with her maid, Hagar. Hagar became pregnant (even though Abraham was said to be 86 years old), proving that Sarah was infecund. Sarah in her jealousy drove Hagar away, but she was found by a well and eventually returned (see page 15). Lacking other men, Lot's daughters initiated incest with their father after his flight from Sodom by getting him drunk (19:33).

A brother had the duty to try to impregnate the wife of a brother who died without leaving a son, so that the first son born to her might succeed to the dead brother's name (Deuteronomy 25:5), thus ensuring that the name was perpetuated. The living brother could be disciplined if he refused this duty. The story of Tamar (38:1–30) illustrates this. Judah chose her as the wife of his eldest son, Er, but Er died before she had conceived by him. Er had two brothers, Onan and Shelah. Onan* refused his fraternal duty by indulging in *coitus interruptus* and was

---

*Onanism was a Victorian euphemism for masturbation but is more correctly applied to *coitus interruptus*

killed by the Lord. Tamar was sent back to her father's house until Shelah was old enough to marry (or at least impregnate) her. In the meantime, Judah's wife died. Judah went on a journey to seek comfort from friends. On the way he met Tamar disguised in a veil, pretending to be a prostitute. Judah asked if he could lie with her and offered a kid in payment. Before agreeing, Tamar obtained a pledge as a promise that he would send the kid. The pledge was Judah's signet and cord* and the staff in his hand. Tamar then had intercourse with him and conceived twins. When Judah heard that she was pregnant, he threatened to burn her as a harlot, but the pledge proved that he was the father. Both twins were shoulder-arm presentations.

LEAH AND RACHEL

Jacob had two wives; both were daughters of Laban, who tricked him, after seven years' work in the expectation of marrying Rachel, into sleeping with Leah. Jacob, having loved Rachel for seven years, must have been very slow 'in the uptake' not to have recognised the difference between the two sisters. Leah became pregnant immediately after intercourse and eventually had six sons and a daughter, but Rachel did not conceive until her maid, Bilhah, had had two sons by Jacob. Zilpah, Leah's maid, also had two sons by Jacob. In the summary (35:23) listing Jacob's progeny, the twelve sons are named, but his daughter, Dinah, is not mentioned.

Mandrake has no pharmacological effect and Leah's use of it as an aphrodisiac to stimulate Jacob to father her fifth son (30:15) was psychological. Nothing definite can be said about the weakness in Leah's eyes (29:17) except that the commonest cause of visual difficulty in young persons is myopia (short-sightedness).

---

*This refers to the cylinder seal which was worn on a cord round the neck.

Considering Jacob's proved potency, Rachel was relatively infertile. Her first son was conceived some time after marriage and her second son, Benjamin, over twenty years after marriage. When Leah and Rachel were travelling with Jacob from Gilead to Shechem *en route* to Hebron, where Jacob was to rejoin Isaac, Jacob, fearing an attack from Esau, put his two wives with their children and maids in the front of the convoy (33:2). Later in the journey, when they were travelling from Bethel to Ephrath, Benjamin was born. Rachel seems to have had a prolonged labour (35:16). As she had had a previous successful delivery her death is unlikely to have been due to obstruction. Other obstetrical causes such as as haemorrhage (which with their reverence for blood the Israelites would have noted) and toxaemia (she had made an exhausting journey) also seem unlikely. Rachel was beautiful (29:17) and a malar flush may have added to her attraction. All this is speculation, but rheumatic heart disease must have been common (see page 96). Malar flush is an early sign of mitral stenosis, which is the commonest valvular lesion of the heart especially in women. The mention of a midwife atttending Rachel's labour suggests some form of specialised assistance. The skill of the Hebrew midwives would have no relation to the professionalism and training of the modern state-certified midwife.

DISLOCATED HIP

Earlier in the journey, just before he met Esau, Jacob sent his family, servants and cattle across the Jordan at Jabbok, where the river is narrow (32:22). He stayed alone on the opposite bank and struggled with an angel all night. When the angel found that he could not win, he touched Jacob in the crotch and Jacob's 'thigh was put out of joint' (32:25). The hip joint is so strong that dislocation is rare. There is, however, a form of anterior dislocation which may (rarely) be produced when a person embarking in a boat hesitates whether to stay on land or get in the boat. It is not uncommon for a person with this type of dislocation to be able to walk. It is conceivable that Jacob sustained a dislocation while stretching to step over stepping or other stones in the Jordan. An alternative and possibly more likely diagnosis because of the slow onset is a femoral neuritis. All movements would be painful, but walking would not be impossible.

BUGGERY

Buggery of an incestuous sort may have been committed by Ham upon Noah (9:22) while he was lying drunk in his tent. After all, he planted the first vineyard and made wine from it (9:21). Noah does not appear to have woken during the act, which, if committed for the first time, would be painful. Noah was either in a very deep sleep, almost a coma, or used to it. Ham seems to have been fortunate, first that he did not develop a consequential *Escherichia coli* urethritis, secondly that he was not stoned to death and thirdly that his son, Canaan, was blamed for it. Even among nomadic people in the desert this seems most extraordinary behaviour and Ham must have been a bisexual as he had four sons.

LOT

Abram and his nephew Lot (son of Haran, brother of Terah, Abram's father) (11:31) went to Egypt via the Negeb, taking their wives, possessions and flocks. To avoid overgrazing the pastures (13:6), Lot went east to the Jordan valley and eventually to Sodom, near which there were deposits of bitumen (14:10). Abraham went to Hebron (13:18). As a result of war among the local tribes, Lot was taken captive but was rescued by Abram. He returned to Sodom but was advised by two angels to take his wife and daughters and escape to the Dead Sea to avoid the destruction of the city by fire (19:15). During the journey, Lot's wife, in the rear of the party, looked back in defiance of the instructions given by the angels, and died (19:26), most probably of heat exhaustion. A speculative theory is that she died of asphyxia, when, as may occur in intense flash fires, the blast of the conflagration or explosion sucks air out of the lungs. Unconsciousness is virtually instantaneous. An even more speculative suggestion is that Mrs Lot was calcified when, as she looked back, a hot blast of air caused the production of calcium ions. Both Abram and Lot had been visited by angels, which raises the question of what are angels.

ANGELS

Angels are messengers of God's will. Except in the Middle Ages, the churches have avoided speculation about their nature. Origen[14] (AD 185–254) said: 'It has also been handed down to us in the teaching that there exist certain angels and good powers, who minister to the salvation of men; but when they were created, and what are their characteristics, no one has in any way made plain.' Much confusion exists because biblical writings do not distinguish between men who act as agents or representatives of the Lord and the convenience of presenting mental perceptions as angels. The latter does not differ from what is said to be the voice of the Lord (see page 102). Feminists will lament that no record of a woman angel exists.

The two angels who sat down and ate with Lot (19:2) and the angel who found Hagar (16:7) were men. Abram's angel (15:7) was probably a man, though some doubt exists about this (15:1). Abraham's three angels (18:1) were men who washed their feet and feasted with him. The angel who sat down under the oak at Ophrah with Gideon was a man (Judges 6:11). Almost certainly Manoah's angel (Judges 13:3) was a man who fathered Samson and refused a meal before making his escape. The angel of Balaam (Numbers 22:23) and also of Joshua (Joshua 5:13) appeared with a drawn sword. So also did the angel who appeared before David at Ornan's threshing-floor (I Chronicles 21:16), who must have been a man of frightening appearance to intimidate David into making a sacrifice. The angel who brought food and water to Elijah (I Kings 19:7) was doubtless a kindly traveller who saw the prophet asleep from exhaustion in the wilderness.

The development of angelology under Persian influence – the Jews were subject to the Persians for two hundred years – is noticeable in the apocalyptic writings. The names of the angels appear at this time, the first ones to be named are Gabriel and Michael in the Book of Daniel. Tobias's angel (Tobit 5:4) who acted as guide and counsellor on the journey to Rages, was said to be Raphael disguised as a man. Angels, thought to be intermediaries between God and man, were also considered as the promulgators of the Law (Jubilees 1:27). This view was accepted in the New Testament (Acts 7:53, Galatians 3:19, Hebrews 2:2). Jesus, following popular tradition, regarded angels as spiritual beings (Matthew 22:30) enjoying the company of God in heaven (Matthew 18:10). In Revelation the role of the angel is paramount and their worship in heaven is the prototype of the worship of the Church on earth.

In the New Testament, Gabriel (see page 203) was a man who almost certainly impregnated two women. The angels who released the Apostles (Acts 5:19), and on another occasion Peter (Acts 12:7), from prison, were friendly soldiers or prison warders. The angel who appeared to Cornelius (Acts 10:3) was someone who knew that Simon, called Peter, was in Joppa.

CIRCUMCISION

Circumcision was the sign of the covenant between God and his chosen people (17:9–14). Traditionally, circumcision was performed by banging the foreskin between two sharp stones (usually of flint) (Joshua 5:2). Zipporah did this to her son as propitiation when Moses was ill (Exodus 4:25). No wonder that men circumcised as adults were still sore after three days (34:25). Later, the Israelites performed the operation by drawing the foreskin through a metal ring until the ring met the glans and slicing it with a knife. Circumcision, performed as it was, must have added to the mortality of infant boys through either haemorrhage or sepsis. Abraham indulged in self-mutilation by performing circumcision on himself at the age of 99 years (17:24). Circumcision was not performed in Mesopotamia, the country from which the Israelites originally came, but the Egyptians seem to have copied it from the negroes of Africa. Circumcision was not general among Egyptian men but was required for priests and was common among shepherds, fishermen and sailors. The Romans tried to suppress it. The Israelites seem to have copied it as a mandatory requirement from the Egyptians. The Egyptians also induldged in clitorectomy for girls,[15] but this operation is insignificant compared with the barbaric infibulation practised in the Sudan, Somalia and Mali even today.

Circumcision has some slight value against cancer of the penis (which anyway is a rare disease) and more importantly against cancer of the cervix in women because of cleaner foreskins. Carcinoma of the cervix is associated with sexual intercourse from an early age, promiscuity and frequent intercourse. In the U.S.A. it is commonest among those in low-income groups, negroes and southern whites.[16] The lower incidence among Jews is probably due to religious prohibitions reducing the frequency of intercourse. The incidence is highest among partners of christian negroes. Considerable evidence is accumulating that Human Papilloma Virus (HPV) infection of the female lower genital tract is causally associated with cancer of the cervix; that this may be transmitted by the male partner and that the presence of penile HPV infection rather than the woman's sexual behaviour *per se* gives rise to the risk of intracervical neoplasm.[17] Obviously frequent and promiscuous intercourse increases the risk of infection. Screening studies in Britain suggest that between 0.7 and 1.5 per hundred of women between the ages of 30 and 40 years may be affected. These figures must be treated with great caution because of the controversy about pre-invasive cancer. The prognosis after early treatment is excellent.

In the Gulf War (1991) some uncircumcised men suffered a balinitis due to irritation by sand accumulated around the prepuce.

HIRSUTISM

Esau was covered with hair when born (25:25) as a twin to his parents, Rebekah and Isaac. His brother Jacob was 'smooth' (27:11). The Hebrew *ḥālaq* can also refer to smoothness or slipperiness or character, a trait Jacob displayed when he deceived his father and stole his brother's birthright (27:18–36). One thing is certain: Esau and Jacob were not identical twins, two separate ova having been fertilised by two separate spermatozoa. Without details of the family history of Isaac and Rebekah nothing more can be said about genetics. Some biblical scholars, according to Sandison and Wells[18], think that Esau may have suffered from hyper-adrenalism, the basis of which idea is more speculative than real. First, Esau survived his birth, secondly he was hirsute at birth and his genitals are not reported to be abnormal, and thirdly he does not appear to have developed further signs of hyper-adrenalism in life. Hairiness of the hands and neck, especially if extended to other parts of the body, which could be mistaken for the hair of kids when Rebekah tricked the dying Isaac (27:16), would put Esau into the class of medical freaks. At any rate Esau and Jacob conformed to the popular but unfounded belief that hirsutism is associated with active pursuits. Esau was a skilful hunter and Jacob was a quiet man.

DREAMS

Joseph was good-looking (39:6) and was bought by Potiphar, one of Pharoah's officers, to serve Pharaoh. Joseph had sufficient sense to reject the advances of Potiphar's wife, who was attracted by his good looks, but Potiphar's wife pretended that he had insulted her and he was imprisoned. This may be the first reported example of sexual harassment. In prison, Joseph correctly interpreted the dreams of Pharaoh's chief baker (40:16 – 19), who was subsequently hanged, seemingly for no good reason, and the chief butler (40:9 – 13), who was restored to his position. Two years later, the butler suggested that Joseph might interpret Pharaoh's dreams about the sleek and gaunt cows (41:2) and about the plump and blighted ears of corn (41:5). Joseph was fetched from prison and his interpretation pleased Pharaoh. He was given the job of controlling the food supply of Egypt, which he did successfully.

In all this Joseph may be seen to have anticipated Sigmund Freud's interpretation of dreams[19], but unlike Freud he failed to appreciate the need to lead the patient to understand his own symptoms. Perhaps that is the reason why Joseph's own dreams caused him so much trouble (37:6,9). Joseph seems to have had sufficient cunning to rise above his fellows, becoming overseer of other prisoners (39:22) and to grasp what Pharaoh wanted of his dreams (41:17 – 24). With or without Joseph's help, Pharaoh acted out his dreams (which, like all dreams, arose from earlier mental processes), deluding the credulous about the prophetic nature of dreams. All this was to Joseph's considerable advantage. Pharaoh's dreams are the earliest and perhaps the best example of the day precipitate dreams[20]. At that time, of course, physicians were no more than the repositories of folklore, soothsaying and herbal remedies. That is not to say that they did not bring comfort and it should be noted that, following the Roman sack of Corinth (c.150BC), when captives from that city were being sold in the Roman slave markets, women with 'medical' knowledge commanded the highest prices.[21]

LIFE EXPECTANCY

Joseph died at the reputed age of 110 years (50:26) and like his father, Jacob (50:3), was embalmed by Egyptian physicians, a technique (taking forty days) which the Egyptians kept very secret and had practised since 3000 BC.[22] Abraham is said to have died aged 175 years (25:7), which, if true, was a noble effort because some years earlier he had taken a second wife, Keturah, who bore him six sons. Sarah, who after Abraham had fathered a child by Hagar (16:3) is said to have borne Isaac at the age of 90 years, is recorded as dying at the age of 127 (23:1), possibly of some form of cardiac arrest after hearing of Abraham's attempt to slaughter Isaac (22:10). The most extreme case is Noah, who is said to have lived for 950 years (9:28). Such ages are absurd. Without an enforced system of birth certificates (such as introduced in Britain in 1872) ages can be determined only by comparison with external and historical public events. Wolff[23] has done this for fourteen kings of the House of David reigning between 926 and 597 BC. No generalisation about life span can be made from such a small and highly selected group, but if the percentage of survivors between the extreme ages (21 and 66 years) is calculated for five-year periods, it will be seen that the graph (Figure 3(a)) suggests that the mortality was similar to that of tumblers broken in a restaurant or of fish (which continue to grow until killed by a predator). The kings died at a rate equivalent to about 3 per hundred a year. In other words, death occurred fortuitously and they had no expectation of life. This is in contrast to modern westernised man, who, after surviving the hazards of childhood and

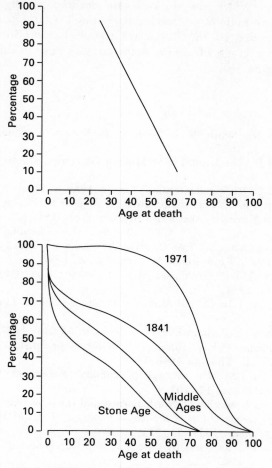

Figure 3(a) Survival rate of fourteen kings of the House of David.

(b) Survival rate of Stone Age population and of population of England and Wales showing 'rectangularisation'. (Clarke[24])

adolescence may expect to survive to about 70 years of age, after which the survival rate declines rapidly. This process is known as 'rectangularisation'. Clarke[24], using data supplied by the Registrar-General, has produced an illustrative graph of approximate survival rates in different eras (Figure 3(b)).

References

1. Robertson Smith W. *Religion of the Semites*. London: A & C. Black, 1927.
2. Baird D. The Evolution of Modern Obstetrics. *Lancet*. 1960, i: 557.
3. Baird D. Perinatal Mortality, *Lancet*. 1969, i: 511.
4. Thompson B., Frazer C., Hewitt A., Stopper D. *Having a First Baby*. Aberdeen: Aberdeen University Press, 1989.
5. Bang R.A., Bang A.T., Baitule M., Choudhary Y., Sarmukaddam S., Tale O. High Prevalence of Gynaecological Diseases in Rural Indian Women. *Lancet*. 1989, i: 85.
6. Briggs N.D., Oruamabo R.S. Technology-free Obstetrics. *Lancet*. 1991, 337: 533.
7. Field M.J. *Angels and Ministers of Grace*. London: Longman, 1971.
8. Poulton J. All about Eve. *New Scientist*. 14 May 1987:51.
9. Montague M.F.A. *Adolescent Sterility*. Springfield, Illinois: Charles C. Thomas, 1946.
10. Duncan J.M. On the age of nubility. *Edinburgh Medical Journal*. 1866, 12, 207.
11. Polunin I. Murats of North Borneo and their Declining Population. *Transactions of the Royal Society of Tropical Medicine and Hygiene*. 1959, 53: 312.
12. Polunin I., Saunders M. Infertility and Depopulation. *Lancet*. 1959, ii: 1005.
13. Bang A.T., Bang R.A., Tale O., Sontakke P., Solanki J., Wargantiwar R., Kelzarkar P. Reduction in pneumonia mortality and total childhood mortality by means of community-based intervention trial in Gadchiroli, India. *Lancet*. 1990, 336: 201.

14. Origen. *De Principiis*, I, Preface, 10. *In: A New Eusebius*, ed. Stevenson, J. London: SPCK, 1978.
15. Sigerist H.E. *A History of Medicine*. New York: Oxford University Press, 1951.
16. Anon. Coitus as a cause of cervical cancer. *Lancet*. 1961, i: 211.
17. Campion M.J., Singer A., Clarkson P.K., McCance P.J. Increased risk of cervical neoplasia in consorts of men with penile condylomata acuminata, *Lancet*. 1985, i: 943.
18. Sandison A.T., Wells D. Endocrine disease. *In: Diseases of Antiquity*, ed. Brothwell D., Sandison A.T. Springfield, Illinois: Charles C. Thomas, 1967.
19. Freud S. *The Interpretation of Dreams*. London: Allen & Unwin, 1922.
20. Kelman H. The Day Precipitate of Pharaoh's Dreams. *Psychoanalytic Quarterly*. 1986, **155**: 306.
21. Bowden R.E.M. Women in Medicine. *The Oxford Companion to Medicine*, ed. Walton, J. Oxford: Oxford University Press, 1986.
22. El Mahdy C. *Mummies, Myth and Magic in Ancient Egypt*. London: Thames & Hudson, 1989.
23. Wolff H.W. *Anthropology of the Old Testament*. London: SCM Press, 1981.
24. Clarke C. Increased Longevity in Man. *Journal of the Royal College of Physicians of London*. 1986, **20**: 122.

2

EXODUS

POPULATION INCREASE

The Israelites in Egypt multiplied so that the land was 'filled with them' (1:7) and they became 'too many and too mighty' (1:9). They cannot have been all that numerous, however, as two midwives met their needs (1:15). Ignoring Pharaoh's instruction (1:16) which, if he wished to limit the Israelite population, should have been to kill baby girls rather than boys as the future population is determined by the number of women of childbearing age, the Hebrew midwives were in demand.

It is interesting to note that the birthing stool was used (1:16). In primitive societies women usually deliver in the squatting position or on the lap of another woman as Bilhah did on Rachel's lap (Genesis 30:3). In Western cultures today the commonest positions used for the second stage of delivery are either the left lateral or supine in bed. The advantages of other positions, including the birthing chair, are now being re-examined. 'Home delivery', or at least delivery within the tribal groups, made the spread of infection (though it undoubtedly occurred) less of a problem than in the last century when hospital delivery became fashionable. In Vienna, the maternal death rate from lying-in fever (puerperal sepsis) reached 30 per cent before Semmelweiss in 1846 showed the need for cleanliness (the

24

principles of sterilisation had not been discovered) and prevented physicians and students attending the lying-in wards from visiting post-mortem rooms. Even though women in labour were helped by one or two friends before the era of the midwife, there is little doubt that they and the child were subject to much abuse and ill-judged intervention. Obstetric forceps had not been invented but if anyone wants to know what could be done in a much later age read Gregory.[1] Remember, too, that Simpson did not introduce chloroform until 1847.

HEBREWS AS SLAVES

The most likely explanation of the reduction of the status of the Hebrews, previously farmers in Goshen (Genesis 47:6), to state slaves is that a new Pharaoh who knew not Joseph (1:8) was frightened of their large number and questionable loyalty (1:10). As slaves they were put to work building the store-cities of Pithom and Ra-amses (1:11).

The bricks for the construction work were made of Nile mud, and chopped straw was used to bind the mud. Puddling mud (especially with the feet) to make bricks (5:7 – 21) in the Delta would be an almost ideal way of contracting bilharzia (infection with *Schistosomiasis haematobium*). The Bible does not make any mention of diseases which might have been bilharzia, a disease which affects nearly all farmers in Egypt today and which was present in Egypt at the time of the Exodus. Whether the Pharaoh of the Exodus was Rameses II (c.1290 – 1224 BC) or his successor Merenptah (c.1224 – 1211 BC) is not important from this point of view. Ova of *S. haematobium* have been found in the kidneys of two mummies dating from the XX Dynasty (c.1185 – 1084 BC).[2] More recently, the calcified remains of a male schistosome have been discovered in a mummy dated about 1500 BC or before Moses was alive.[3] Fossils of *Bulinus truncatus*, an

essential link in the life cycle of the schistosome, have been
found in the brickwork of Tel-Aquir in Mesopotamia.

Eggs of the schistosome are passed in human urine (and
occasionally in faeces). When urine is diluted with water
these release miracidia which enter a snail (*Bulinus truncatus*).
In the snail they develop into spirocysts which eventually are
released into the water. After changing into cercariae they
penetrate the skin of man, pass through the tissues, reach
the lungs and through the veins reach the portal system of
the liver. Here the female (about 20 mm long) is impregnated
by lying in the curvature of the male (about 13 mm long).
Eggs are produced and these, via the bloodstream, settle
in the walls of the bladder and the rectum. Bilharzia
is a most debilitating disease with far-reaching economic
consequences. Urinary symptoms include low abdominal pain
and haematuria (blood in the urine), which commonly is so
gross as to cause anaemia through blood loss, and the intense
tissue reaction often results in cancer of the bladder. Venous
obstruction may produce portal hypertension (back pressure
in the veins of the liver), oesophageal varices (dilated veins in
the gullet) and ascites (fluid in the abdomen). Until recently,
when praziquantel was introduced, treatment was not very
effective. The snail (*B. truncatus*) likes slow-running streams
and ponds such as occur in irrigation systems. Theoretically
it should be possible to control the snails, but practically this
is impossible. Repeat treatment of exposed persons such as
farmers with praziquantel will break the cycle and eventually
eliminate the disease.

The Hebrews were farmers and to a lesser extent brick-
makers. Both jobs would require the exposure of bare
legs to water: farming by irrigating crops, and brick-
making by digging silt out of the channels which form
the Delta. The passing of wine-coloured urine would
have been quickly noticed and alarming. Why such a
debilitating and painful disease with obvious symptoms
is not reported in Exodus is inexplicable. If the Israelites
did suffer from schistosomiasis it would die out in one

generation in the wilderness, which would be hostile to *B. truncatus*.

MOSES'S MISSION (see page 98)

While Moses was watching his father-in-law's sheep, possibly dreaming but certainly bored (he was after all a man of attainment and used to a much more exciting life), he underwent psychic dissociation (discussed on page 244) which he interpreted as the voice of the Lord (3:2). The subsequent lengthy account of his conversation with the Lord is reminiscent of visual display of dreams (3:8). His mission is to bring the people of Israel out of Egypt and he must go to Pharaoh and ask for their release. Moses asks for a sign which he might use to prove to the Israelites that he has received his instructions from God. He is given the sign of the rod-serpent and that of the leprous hand (4:6 – 8). Moses's hand is referred to as 'being leprous, white as snow'. The Hebrew text describes the hand as 'being leprous, as snow'; the epithet 'white' was added by later translators. This is discussed on page 52. Moses used the trick of the rod-serpent when he and Aaron appeared before the Pharaoh (7:10), but there is no record of him using the sign of the leprous hand.

THE PLAGUES

After Pharaoh had refused the request of Moses that the people of Israel should be allowed to emigrate, Egypt was afflicted with ten plagues. The modern reader has many difficulties in accepting the stories of the plagues and these difficulties are enhanced by the claim that none of the plagues touched the Israelites as the Lord made 'a distinction' between them and the Egyptians (11:7). The most likely possibility is that the plagues were natural events* which the Israelites, looking back over their history, interpreted as bearing witness to the power of God in redeeming them from their bondage in Egypt. Some of the plagues have a medical interest.

1. The Nile turned to blood (7:16–24)

Pseudomonas are a group of bacteria which produce fluorescent pigments which in culture diffuse into the medium. Before antibiotics, *P. aeruginosa* was the occasional cause of blue-green pus in wounds into which it had been accidentally introduced. Among the many members of this group of bacteria, *P. cepacia* is present in soil and is capable of rapid multiplication. A wild speculation is that fluorescent pigments from *P. cepacia* diffused into the Nile, coloured the dust and protozoa present in the water, and in the reflection of sunlight caused it to have a red appearance (7:20). The upper reaches of the Nile are rapid flowing, but in the Delta the flow may have been sufficiently low to allow a film of dust on the water to help the reflection. The Israelites indulged in much hyperbole and the colouring of a few stagnant pools along the edges of the Nile would be sufficient. A similar incident is recorded in II Kings 3:22. When the dried-up bed of a stream near Edom suddenly filled with water, the Moabites, looking at the water early one morning, thought the water was blood. The sun caused a red reflection. The surprising fact is that the Israelites and Moabites, both used to a nomadic

*Recent attempts[4] to link the volcanic explosion of Thera with the plagues must remain conjectural pending more accurate dating. The dates for the eruption of Thera vary between 2590–1100 BC. The Exodus probably took place c. 1260 BC. If accurate dates can be established, the pillar of fire (13:12) and the reddening of the Nile by dust (7:16) may be associated. The cloud of dust must have obscured the sun for a considerable time to have had any relation to the deaths of the first born.

life, should mistake the red reflection for blood. Perhaps, on both occasions, they were deceived by a much more intense colouring than usual.

2. Frogs (8:2 – 15)

Seven days after this incident, a population explosion of frogs occurred (8:3), also suggesting some unusual climatic conditions. As with all such explosions the food supply became insufficient, many of the frogs died and 'the land stank' (8:14).

3. Gnats and flies (8:16 – 32)

As might be expected an epidemic of gnats (8:17) and flies (8:21) followed the contagion of dead frogs. Gnats and flies are members of the very large order of *Diptera* (two-winged insects) which also includes mosquitoes. Gnats have no precise definition but are regarded as small insects or midges; upwards of fifty species are known.

Phlebotomus or sand-flies are minute, often as small as 1.5 mm. Only the females suck blood and the bite is very irritating. They bite at night, resting during the day. *Phlebotomus* carries dengue (three-day fever). Some limit their choice to man (*P. argentipes* in India) and warm-blooded mammals, but others not only attack man but feed on frogs, lizards, snakes and even tarantulas. Males feed on organic matter; they can suck from vegetation, earth or even the sweat of man. The distribution of *Phlebotomus* is sporadic, being limited by being able to find resting-places, such as crevices in walls, under furniture, or behind pictures during the day. *Phlebotomus* is silent in flight and being so small can penetrate mosquito nets.

An even more irritating gnat is *Simulium* (or black-fly). The adult is about 4 mm in length; only the female sucks blood but bites during the day. *Simulia* abound in running water as favoured by fishermen and in favourable

circumstances occur in astronomical numbers. A swarm of
Simulia can be vicious in their attack and the consequent
irritation of distressing intensity; indeed, the appearance of
a victim may simulate erysipelas. During the earlier years of
this century *Simulia* were a particular pest along the Nile.
There are well-authenticated reports from both the U.S.A.
and Romania of the death of cattle, pigs, horses, sheep and
goats after being attacked by *Simulia*. In tropical Africa,
especially feared is *S. damnosum* because of the irritation
and swelling at the site of a bite.

Also, in sub-tropical Africa, *Simulia* are the vector of
onchocerca causing river blindness, a disease in which
microfilariae circulate in the blood. Besides causing nodules
in the skin and sub-cutaneous tissues, living *microfilariae*
may be found in the cornea and anterior chamber of the
eye. In the cornea nummular opacities occur, but in the
anterior chamber little or no trouble occurs so long as the
microfilariae are alive. When dead they fall to the bottom
and start a fibrous reaction which may involve the iris and
ultimately result in glaucoma and blindness.

Like all pastoral and nomadic people the Israelites would
have been acute observers of nature, certainly more so than
is recorded in the Scriptures, so that mosquitoes are unlikely
to have been mistaken for gnats.

Anopheles breed in clear water such as lakes fed by running
streams or springs, but *Culex* and *Aedes* (one species of the
latter is known as *A. egypti*) usually breed in stagnant water
like that found in a jar or bowl filled with rain or nowadays
in discarded tyres. *Culex* is capable of breeding in dirty water
such as cesspits. *Anopheles* are the vector of malaria, *Culex*
of filiarisis and dengue, *Aedes* of dengue and yellow fever.
With the exception of yellow fever all these diseases are
present in the Middle East today and are likely to have
been present in biblical times. Their importance need not be
emphasised, though there is no specific reference to illnesses
of the sort which might be ascribed to them.

House-flies (*Musca domestica*) are 8 – 9 mm long when
adult, breed in decaying organic matter and particularly

favour human and animal excrement. In warm or temperate climates *M. domestica* may lie dormant over the winter. One male and one female may produce five billion offspring in a season. Not all survive, though plenty do. Eggs hatch in 9 – 24 hours and the larval and pupal stages together take 10 – 14 days. *M. domestica* does not bite, but its sticky, hairy legs, constant defecation and frequent regurgitation make it an ideal vehicle for the passive transference of infection. *M. domestica* feeds on almost anything from excrement, putrefying matter, open sores, sputum, milk and animal or human food. As its name implies, *M. domestica* prefers domestic houses. As a rule it does not travel more than a quarter of a mile in an area of dense housing. In wind, *M. domestica* travels across or against it and has been reliably recorded as covering 13 miles (21 km).

One other fly which may have been important, though not specifically mentioned in biblical times, is the botfly *Muscida*: *M. gastrophilinae* feeds on horses, *M. oestridae* on sheep, cattle and deer, and *M. cuterebrae* on rodents. Botflies have a very penetrating bite, especially important in stampeding cattle and horses and spoiling their skin. Most bite man, but only *M. gastrophilinae* cause specific lesions, creeping eruptions due to larvae under the skin. Botflies may have accounted for the cattle plague.

4. Death of the first born (12:1 – 35)

Gnats (*Phlebotomus* and *Simulium*) because of their breeding and feeding habits would have no preference in biting Egyptians or Israelites. Indeed, this seems to have been the case when Aaron struck the dusty earth with his rod and there came gnats on man and beast (8:17). Piles of rotting frogs would have been an ideal place for breeding besides being a good medium for the multiplication of bacteria. The Israelites were not affected by flies (8:24). The need to mark the lintels of the houses (12:7) before the visitation which killed the Egyptian first born suggests that the Israelites were living muddled up with the Egyptians. For the Israelites to escape infection, if indeed they did, some micro-domestic environment must have afforded protection. The Israelites were a clean people, enjoined to wash (Jeremiah 2:22). The injunction in verse 12:10 (and similar instructions in 29:34, Leviticus 7:15 and Numbers 9:12) about eating food on the same day that it was roasted and burning anything left over would remove a source of food for flies and also markedly lessen the chances of gastro-intestinal infection. The cleanliness of the Israelites in disposing of left-over food and keeping food covered would reduce the attraction of their houses to flies. This may have accounted for the safety of the first-born Israelites (12:9, 12), especially when associated with meticulous care of the first born.

The instruction (23:19, 34:26) not to boil a kid in its mother's milk has nothing to do with hygiene, but with the idea, common among pastoral tribes, that milk and meat should not be eaten together (or indeed cooked together) lest the animal that gave the milk should die. The basis of this idea may have been that it was bad husbandry. Goats and sheep are fit to lactate only in the period soon after the green flush following the rainy season. To kill kids would extinguish the stock. The instruction is repeated in Deuteronomy 14:21, the second set of commandments given by the Lord to Moses after the first tablets had been broken (32:19).

A similar argument about cleanliness might apply to cattle if the Israelites kept their byres cleaner than the Egyptians. Egyptian cattle, especially calves, might be supposed to have died of scours, an intestinal infection with *Escherichia coli* (previously known as *Bacterium coli*), which establish themselves in the gut within a few days of birth in both man and animals. *E. coli* have a very complex antigenic pattern and may become pathogenic, though usually they are no more than an index of faecal contamination. Desirably, drinking water should not contain any *E. coli*, but up to three organisms per ml may be regarded as satisfactory.

5. Boils and sores (9:8–11)

The story of boils arising after Moses scattered the ashes of a kiln seems a little far-fetched. Anthrax is unlikely, as even spores would be destroyed in a kiln. If the ashes were from a lime-kiln (which is possible as lime is required for mortar) the dust of quicklime might cause irritation of the skin in those nearby. Intense irritation of the conjunctivae would also occur and this is not mentioned. Interesting confirmation that the Israelites were able to obtain temperatures of just over 1000°C (see pages 57 and 138) is provided by their ability to work gold, silver and bronze (25:3) and to make ornaments (31:2ff., 32:2). Gold melts at 1062°C, silver at 960°C and tin, a constituent of bronze, at 232°C. Dust control from kilns seems to have been deficient by modern standards because the cloud which engulfed Mount Sinai is likened to the smoke from a kiln (19:18). This suggests that kilns, whether for lime or smelting metal, were fairly common.

THE EXODUS

Eventually the people of Israel were allowed to leave Egypt under the leadership of Moses and, after years of wandering in the desert, reached the promised land of Canaan. Extra-biblical evidence that the Israelites were in Canaan by the second half of the thirteenth century BC is provided by the Merneptah stele.[5] Inscribed about 1230 BC, it recounts the Pharaoh's victories over his enemies and the section dealing with Canaan includes the line 'Israel* is desolate; its seed is no more.' This supports the view that the Exodus took place in the first half of the thirteenth century BC. For the Exodus itself there is no extra-biblical evidence. But the witness of the Bible is so imperative that there can be no

---

*In this context 'Israel' refers to a population group and not a region.

doubt that some remarkable event took place. Israel has remembered the Exodus as the constitutive event that called her into being as a nation. It has stood at the centre of her confession of faith from the beginning, as is witnessed by certain ancient poems (15:1 – 18) and credos (Deuteronomy 6:20 – 25) that go back to the earliest period of her history. Nevertheless, the biblical account is not credible as it stands.

MIXED MULTITUDE

To start with, the numbers taking part in the Exodus have been grossly exaggerated. The logistics of moving 600,000 men on foot together with their wives, children and cattle as recounted in Chapter 12 stretches the imagination to incredulity. Also, this does not square with the information (1:15 – 20) that two midwives served the whole Hebrew colony in Egypt. The record is correct, however, in saying that they were a motley group, not only the tribes of Israel but a 'mixed multitude'. Such a rabble would be unlikely to make much speed, at the most 1 mile (1.6 km) per hour. Even if walking five abreast with their cattle, they would take 230 hours or nearly ten days to pass one point.[6] Most probably they left in small tribal or family groups.

WATER

Supplying water to a multitude of more than 600,000 would have been an impossibility. The British army allows 5 gallons (22.7 litres) of water per man per day on campaigns, 1 gallon (4.5 litres) of which is for cooking and drinking. In hot climates the amount of drinking water may have to be increased to 2 or 3 gallons (9 or 13.5 litres). As beer drinkers know, the body does not store water, but the amount of water in the body is maintained within precise limits. The body of an 11 stone (70 kg) man contains 70 pints (42 litres) of water. Water is acquired by drink, by food and by oxidation of hydrogen in foodstuffs. Water is lost through the kidneys, which have to excrete about 3 pints (1.5 litres) a day to remove waste products from the body (obligatory excretion). A small amount is lost through the bowel and a substantial amount through expired air, depending on the climate. The amount lost through sweat is determined by physical exertion and the ambient temperature and humidity.

A soldier wearing battle kit marching on a warm day in a temperate climate may lose 0.9 pints (0.5 litres) of water as sweat in one hour. In climates such as Aden 17.6 pints (10 litres) of water may be lost in a day. In some extreme circumstances up to 21 pints (12 litres) may be lost as sweat.

A deficiency of 3.5 pints (2 litres) in body water causes marked thirst, at 7 pints (4 litres) deficiency serious illness supervenes and death will almost certainly occur before the deficiency reaches 14 pints (8 litres). At these rates of loss, unless water is replaced, death will ensue within twelve hours.

Besides the need to replace water, salt is also needed and drinking saline solution (1 per cent salt in water or approximately one teaspoon in a pint) is preferable if the sweat rate has been high. Alternatively, up to ¾oz (20 g) of salt may be added to the food and drink over twenty-four hours. Salt tablets are undesirable as they may not be absorbed.

Meandering at night (when it can be very cold in the desert) with a slow speed at day to reduce water requirements, and rationed to ½ gallon (2.25 litres) for 600,000 men, 600,000 women and 1,200,00 children (one woman for each man and two children for each woman), a total of 1,200,000 gallons (5,200,000 litres) or 5357 tons of water would be needed each day. This means that each woman (men are unlikely to have carried anything) would have to carry an extra 18.5 lb (8.4 kg) at the start of every day. These allowances take no account of the water required for livestock. There is no evidence about the time of year when the Exodus took place. Perhaps small groups travelled over a lengthy period. For this reason there is no point in trying to calculate whether water requirements were more or less at different months. There is no mention of how the water was distributed, if indeed there was need for formal distribution among family and tribal parties.

When the assembled rabble reached Marah in the desert of Shur, they had been without water for three days (15:23), near the limit of survival. Even if the water became sweet when Moses threw a tree into it, no record is given of how the problem of distribution was solved. Even Elim (15:27), which had twelve springs and seventy palm trees, would be inadequate for some 2,400,000 persons and their stock.

MANNA AND QUAILS

Later, hunger was satisfied by eating manna (which is the extruded sap of the *Tamarix gallica* tree (16:14). Manna seems to have appeared fairly frequently (Joshua 5:12). Quails (which fly so low that they are easily caught) were also eaten. This account of the consumption of quails provides an interesting comparison with the story of the devastation caused by eating poisoned quails (see page 75).

HYGIENE

Hygiene on the march and at resting-places must have been appalling. The disposal of faeces and urine from 2,400,000 persons (equivalent to the population of Paris or Greater Manchester) is a major task.

MOUNT SINAI

Despite all the hardships of the journey, the people of Istael arrived at Mount Sinai. There the Lord made a covenant with them whereby they would be his people and he would be their God, provided they obeyed his commandments in every respect. Before meeting God on Mount Sinai, Moses consecrated the people and ordered them to abstain from sexual intercourse (19:15) as this would make them ritually unclean (Leviticus 15:16ff.).

Moses is said to have been with the Lord on Mount Sinai for forty days without eating bread or drinking water (24:18). Fasting without food and water for forty days and forty nights is an extreme feat, even more prodigious when followed by carrying two tablets of stone down the mountain in a hurry as Moses is said to have done (32:15). When he came down he rebuked Aaron and the people for having made the golden calf and took the calf and destroyed it. If he was well enough to do this he must have eaten something and he certainly did not go without water, even if this was imbibed in a disguised form (see page 34). When Moses returned to the camp after a second fast of forty days and forty nights on Mount Sinai, the skin of his face was shining (34:29). The sun emits a wide spectrum of electro-magnetic waves. Only a limited range of these are visible. Infra-red waves are felt as heat; the relatively long ultra violet light (UVL) is filtered by the atmosphere. Mount Sinai is 7400 feet (2260 m) high. At that height the atmosphere is becoming rarified compared with lower altitudes where the UVL is filtered out, especially by ozone and water vapour. We are not told how far Moses ascended, but we are told that the Lord descended and formed a cloud (24:16). Even so, Moses may well have been affected by the sunlight and experienced the heat of infra-red rays. Desquamation of the skin with underlying redness due to dilation of the arterioles could have been caused so that ecstacy at speaking with the Lord may not have been the only cause of his shining face.

The commandments which Moses brought down from the mountain and which are given in detail in Exodus and the other books of the Pentateuch cover all aspects of social and religious life. Rules are laid down for the construction of the altar, the dress of the priests and the building of the tabernacle. The altar could be of earth or uncut stone (20:21ff.). It had to be without steps, so there was no risk of the priest exposing his genitals when he approached the altar. Later, when an altar with steps was constructed, the priest had to wear linen breeches to preserve his modesty (28:42), by which it may be inferred that clothes were sparse.

PHARMACEUTICAL MONOPOLY

In prescribing the composition of the anointing oil and the incense so precisely (30:22ff.), Moses established a pharmaceutical monopoly which might well be the envy of the present-day industry.

EAR PIERCING

Piercing the ear with an awl (21:6) must have been very painful, but was endured by slaves so that they could stay with their wives and their masters. Ears were also pierced for ornament (32:2) and it is unlikely that a much sharper instrument was used. Ear piercing, unless done under aseptic conditions, is dangerous. Besides sloughing of the lobe because of sepsis, hepatitis-B and AIDS may be transmitted today.

CONSTRUCTION OF THE ARK OF THE COVENANT

Goats' hair, rams' skins (tanned and untanned) and goatskin used to build the ark of the covenant are a potent source of anthrax (25:5; 35:7; 26). Spores of *Bacillus anthrax* are ubiquitous. Wool, horsehair, camel hair, hides, bones and bonemeal are all sources of anthrax. Imports into Britain from the Middle East, Pakistan and India are especially suspect though no country can be excluded. Spores are very persistent in the soil, but in Britain not at excessive levels. When soil and vegetation become heavily infected, the hazard of infection is increased. Gruinard Island, off the west coast of Scotland, was used for experiments involving anthrax during the Second World War. In 1987 disinfection reduced infection to an acceptable level. For those interested in tedious tables the Report of the Committee of Inquiry on Anthrax[7] may be worth studying.

The two cherubim made of hammered gold (25:18) guarding the ark bear no relation to the cherubs of popular imagination. Nevertheless, they are reminiscent of a story, probably anecdotal, common among medical students, that mediaeval popes, to improve the splendour of their entertainment, covered infants with gold leaf to imitate cherubs. They all died. Besides the need to replace water, there is a need to lose water through the skin, which by evaporation cools and avoids hyperthermia.

MURDER

Murder, even if not actually committed, is the recommended punishment for working on the Sabbath (31:15), which is in striking contrast to God's commandment 'You shall not kill' (20:13). Murder to the extent of genocide ordered by Moses (32:27), if really carried out (3000 dead men), seems a very excessive retribution for making a golden calf. At the very least Aaron connived by collecting jewellery (32:3). Next day, Moses did not show guilt at ordering such a slaughter, but instead at the sin of making the calf. If the plague which the Lord sent as a punishment (32:35) had a physical cause, no details are given which would allow it to be recognised. More likely, it was collective guilt for murder and distress at the carnage. No account of burial is given.

HEALTH

One of the benefits of keeping the commandments of the Lord was good health (23:25). This implies that sickness (which today we would say had a large psychosomatic element) was a communal affair, which could be cured by strict observance of the commandments of God by the community. Such an attitude is important in relation to leprosy (see page 45).

The sins of the guilty, which presumably resulted in disease, would be visited upon their children to the third and fourth generations (34:7). Inherited disease would not stop so soon, but probably this was as long as memory lasted in the absence of precise records. In view of the long family trees in the first six chapters of I Chronicles, this may have been a dire threat.

HORNETS

Hornets (23:28), which the Lord said he would use to drive out the Hivites, Canaanites and Hittites, are members of the order of *Hymenoptera* which also includes bees and wasps.

Hymenoptera have two membranous wings on each side and comprise more than 50,000 species. A few neither sting nor bite, but most do. Bites are sometimes worse than stings. Wasps and hornets are especially feared because of their sting. The venom contains specific toxins and in some cases hydroxytryptamine. The bumblebee (like wasps or hornets) retains its lance; with other species the lance or sting should be removed by scraping it out with a blade or a fingernail. Forceps should not be used. To kill an unsensitised adult hundreds of stings are needed. Death has been recorded after thirty stings and recovery after over two thousand.[8] About 0.5 per cent of the population are hypersensitive to bee and wasp stings. As such persons may become unconscious, they should wear a suitably inscribed tag.

LAND OF CANAAN

When the Hebrews entered Canaan, they did so as a loose confederation of clans and found there people of the same race with a similar language whom they were unable to conquer. The Canaanites, who had a sophisticated culture, continued to live in the cities and villages in the valleys and the Israelites co-existed, intermingling and intermarrying but living in the hills.[9]

References

1. Gregory P. Women, childbirth and medicine. *St. Thomas's Hospital Gazette*. 1985, 83.
2. Ruffer M.A. Note on the presence of 'Bilharzia haematobia' in Egyptian mummies of the Twentieth Dynasty (1250 – 1000 BC). *British Medical Journal*. 1910, i: 16.
3. Isherwood I., Jarvis H., Fawcett R.A. *Manchester Museum Mummy Project,* ed. David A.R. Manchester: Manchester University Press, 1979.
4. Wilson I. *The Exodus Enigma*. London: Weidenfeld & Nicolson, 1985.
5. Jones E. *Discoveries and Documents*. London: Epworth Press, 1974.
6. Herbert G. *When Israel came out of Egypt*. London: SCM Press, 1961.
7. *Report of the Committee of Inquiry on Anthrax*. Cmnd 846. London: HMSO, 1959.
8. Warrell D.A. *Oxford Textbook of Medicine*, Vol. I. Oxford: Oxford University Press, 1983, 6: 44.
9. Blunt A.W.F. *Israel Before Christ*. Oxford: Oxford University Press, 1924.

3

LEVITICUS

Much of Leviticus is tedious repetition of ritual which seems to be designed to separate the Israelites from similar peoples. It does, however, recount the sudden death of two of Aaron's sons and describes the fate awaiting lepers.

MURDER BEFORE THE LORD

Aaron had four sons. In order of seniority they were Nadab, Abihu, Eleazar and Ithamar and, being the sons of Aaron, they were all priests.

Nadab and Abihu 'died before the Lord' with seemingly little commotion after burning incense and offering 'unholy' fire (10:2). 'Unholy' is a potentially misleading rendering of the Hebrew *zārāh*, which includes the sense of strange or alien.

Trying to account for the sudden death of two brothers from natural causes when they were carrying out their normal duties without difficulty supposes a coincidence beyond any reasonable probability. No clinical details of the deaths are given and there is no suggestion of previous disease.

The sudden death of healthy young athletes is uncommon though well recorded. These deaths are thought to be due to symptomless and usually minor atheroma of the coronary arteries. A few deaths are thought to be due to neural influences. Nadab and Abihu may have suffered damage to their hearts as a result of earlier rheumatic fever (see page 96) and a scarcely sustainable hypothesis is that fear and trepidation at Moses's formidable anger was sufficient to cause cardiac arrest. The speed with which the corpses were removed suggests that someone may have known more than they would have liked to admit. The casual references to these deaths in Numbers 3:4 and 26:61 raises suspicion. That two apparently healthy young males should die in this way in the same incident is highly improbable. Homicide remains the favoured diagnosis.

Eleazar, Aaron's third son, had the motive, means and opportunity to carry out the murders. The rule of primogeniture which operated when Nadab and Abihu accompanied Moses, Aaron and seventy elders of Israel to Mount Sinai (Exodus 24:1, 9) would provide an ambitious young man with ample motive. After the death of his brothers, Eleazar's career developed rapidly. He succeeded Aaron as High Priest, became Moses's coadjutor and played an important part in the selection of Joshua as successor to Moses.

The censers used by Nadab and Abihu for burning incense were individual ones made of bronze, rather like small frying-pans with a hollow handle opening into the bowl. Such artefacts dating from between 1000 – 600 BC have been found in Palestine and Syria.[1] Hot charcoal was placed in the bowl, the incense was sprinkled on top and the priest blew down the handle to keep the fire burning and vaporise the incense.

Nadab and Abihu died because the incense in the censers had been contaminated. The preparation of the incense was a priestly monopoly and the penalty was death for anyone else who tried to make it (Exodus 30:38). After the deaths of Nadab and Abihu, it is recorded that Eleazar was in charge of the fragrant incense (Numbers 4:16). Whether he had this responsibility at the time of his brothers' death is not known, but in any case as a priest he had ample opportunity for contaminating the incense at source.

Incense, made from equal parts of stacte, onycha,* galbanum and frankincense beaten together with salt (Exodus 30:34), would be both rare and expensive. Only a small quantity, not much more than a pinch, would be used in each censer. Incense is vaporised, not burned.

If Eleazar contaminated the incense, he would, in the absence of technology, have had to rely on a vegetable poison. If Leviticus 10:9, which prohibits priests from drinking wine or strong drink before undertaking their priestly duties, has any relevance, Nadab and Abihu were thought to be drunk. This rules out monkshood, hellebore (see page 75) and prussic acid − if it could be obtained from cherry kernels in a high enough concentration − as causes. Aconitine is distingushed by tingling of the teeth, hellebore (veratrine) by vomiting almost immediately after ingestion and prussic acid by sudden death. Hemlock (*Conium maculatum*), which grows in the Eastern Mediterranean, is very poisonous[2] and causes muscular paralysis starting peripherally in the limbs. Symptoms like these would easily be mistaken for drunkenness due to alcohol.

Socrates (*c.* 470−399 BC) was condemned (for corrupting the young by introducing new gods) to drink a decoction of hemlock. Plato, describing his death, wrote:[3]

'Socrates walked about, and presently, saying that his legs were heavy, lay down on his back − that was what the man recommended. The man (he was the same one who had administered the poison) kept his hand upon Socrates, and after a little while examined his feet and legs; then pinched his foot hard and asked if he felt it. Socrates said no. Then

---

*Obtained from the operculum of a species of *Strombus*, a marine mollusc, which emits a fragrant odour when burned. The inclusion of onycha implies considerable biological knowledge, even if this was on the part of the Philistines.

he did the same to his legs; and moving gradually upwards
in this way let us see that he was getting cold and numb.
Presently he felt him again and said that when it reached
the heart, Socrates would be gone.'

Hemlock leaves contain 0.2 per cent of coniium (the
main active alkaloid). The juice of hemlock fruits, which
are about a quarter-inch (7 mm) long, contains 2.5 per cent
of coniium. A piece of plant half an inch (1.5 cm) square
is reported from the U.S.A. as causing death in children
when swallowed.[4] Coniium is a piperidine and as such is
heat stable. It boils at 166°C and when dropped on to hot
charcoal would vaporise to form a cloud. If inhaled this
would be highly toxic. The juice of a few seeds would be
fatal. To ensure even distribution in the incense, the fruits
would have to be macerated and this would make both their
incorporation and disguise easier. Maceration would itself be
potentially lethal.

After the deaths of Nadab and Abihu, Aaron, clearly in a
state of shock, did not reply to Moses's pious words about
the Lord needing holy people near him. The corpses were
removed without ceremony, still clad in their priestly linen
tunics. The fire coming from 'the presence of the Lord' had
not burnt the tunics.

It is difficult to avoid the conclusion that Eleazar's
nefarious use of coniium-contaminated incense, possibly at
the instigation of Moses, also played a part in the suppression
of the rebellion of the men of Korah (see page 79).

LEPROSY – ṣāraʻath

Leviticus 13:1–44 describes six different appearances of the
skin as *ṣāraʻath*, a word usually translated as leprosy.
This condition, when diagnosed by a priest, if necessary
after re-examination over a period of fourteen days, made
the sufferer, if an Israelite, ritually unclean. The sufferer had
to adopt the posture of a mourner by tearing his clothes,

allowing his hair to become unkempt and covering his beard or moustache. He was an outcast, forced to dwell outside the camp and to cry 'Unclean, unclean' so that everyone could avoid him.

On recovery from his ṣāra'ath, the individual had to undergo ritual cleansing which involved both a purification rite and the offering of four sacrifices (14:1–32). The purification rite, which also involved sacrifice, was carried out by the local priest, but after Josiah's reforms of 621 BC the four sacrifices could be offered only in the Temple in Jerusalem. It was only after these cleansing ceremonies that the outcast could be received back in society. The elaborate ceremonies of the purification rite and the four sacrifices were prescribed only for the person who was cured of ṣāra'ath and not for those who had recovered from other diseases. In the New Testament, leprosy, unlike all other diseases, is referred to as being cleansed, not cured.

DIAGNOSIS OF ṣāra'ath

Many attempts have been made to find a modern equivalent to ṣāra'ath, but none has proved satisfactory. This is partly due to the vagueness of the clinical details in Leviticus and also to the fact that many of the words used to describe the signs of ṣāra'ath are not found elsewhere in the Old Testament. Suggestions include scabies, ringworm, pityriasis rosea, eczema and favus. Whatever ṣāra'ath was, it was not leprosy as we understand it today, i.e. mycobacterial leprosy. There are two main reasons for this. First, provision is made in Leviticus for recovery. Mycobacterial leprosy was inexorably progressive until the introduction of dapsone in 1947. (Indeterminate leprosy is discussed on page 50). Secondly, mycobacterial leprosy was not present in the Middle East when the contents of Leviticus reached their final form, the latest date for which is during or just after the exile in Babylon (587–538 BC).

After the return from exile the Jews survived as a nation because of their adherence to the precepts of the Mosaic law as set out in the Pentateuch. The law was believed to have been delivered to Moses by God on Mount Sinai; it was therefore of divine origin and any breaches were automatically sacrilege. There must have been inevitable anxiety arising from the fear that an individual or the community had sinned, or, worse still, might have sinned, by failing to observe or by breaking one of the provisions of the law.

The absolute supremacy of the law is to be seen in the Book of Jubilees,[5] which, written between 135 and 105 BC, is the triumphant manifesto of legalism. The author argues that the law is of everlasting validity, the realisation in time of what was timeless and eternal, the complete and ultimate expression of absolute truth. The ideal of the faithful Jew is to be realised in the strict observance of the moral and ritual precepts of the law. Punishments for transgressors are severe.

Lloyd Davies[6,7] has argued that ṣāra'ath was a neuro-dermatitis induced by the stress of living in a society in which every action was, or should have been, determined by a God-given law. Any skin condition that remotely resembled ṣāra'ath would be looked on by the sufferer and others as a punishment and the psychic tension that this would arouse would ensure that the condition was maintained. Anxiety is a major cause of dermatitis; it alone will cause dermatitis. Any concurrent physical trauma arising from an agricultural existence or washing with lye (see page 95) would, of course, make the condition worse. Once the emotional tension is released the skin lesions heal with surprising rapidity.

TRANSLATION OF ṣāra'ath

Mycobacterial leprosy was recognised as a new disease by the Greek physicians in the second and third centuries BC

Table 1. Mycobacterial leprosy: terminology

Date	Language	
587 – 538 BC	Hebrew	*ṣāra'ath*
250 BC	Greek	*lepra*
AD 400	Latin	*lepra*
AD 1382	English	leprosie
AD 1611	English	leprosy (Authorised Version)
AD 1952	English	leprosy (Revised Standard Version)
AD 1970	English	malignant skin disease (New English Bible)

and given the name *elephantiasis graecorum* because of the thickening of the skin. (Filiarial *elephantiasis* was known as *elephantiasis arabum*.) How then did *elephantiasis* become known as leprosy? In part the answer lies in the translation of *ṣāra'ath* (see Table 1). When the Old Testament was translated into Hellenistic Greek about 250 BC, a version which became known as the Septuagint, the word *ṣāra'ath* was rendered as *lepra*, a generic term applied to skin lesions, generally of a scaly nature.* The first Latin translations were made from the Greek version and the translators simply transliterated the Greek *lepra*. Jerome (AD 342 – 420) translated the Old Testament into Latin from the Hebrew and he retained the word *lepra* as the equivalent of *ṣāra'ath*. When the Old Testament was translated into English first from the Latin (1382) and then from the Hebrew (1530), *lepra* was simply taken over as leprosie, and leprosy became firmly established as the English equivalent of *ṣāra'ath* both in the Authorised Version (1611) and the Revised Standard Version (1952) of the Bible. The New English Bible (1970) translated *ṣāra'ath* as 'a malignant skin-disease'. This phrase is open to objection. 'Malignant'

---

*Mycobacterial leprosy is not characterised by scaliness.

is a term which has acquired a precise meaning. In skin conditions it would only apply to cancer, two forms of which are epithelioma and rodent ulcer. In these two instances the translation might be acceptable, but it would be highly misleading if applied to other conditions.

Gradually, by a process which can only be guessed at, *elephantiasis* became known as *lepra*. Part of the reason was that both terms referred to unsightly skin conditions and the word *lepra* was shorter and much easier to use than *elephantiasis*. Whatever the reason, by the fourth century the words were synonymous and were used to describe both leprosy and other skin conditions. Eventually *lepra* was accepted as the name for *elephantiasis graecorum* and *elephantiasis* was used to describe a different disease: thus confusing the matter still further. As a result of this linguistic confusion the Levitical restrictions on ṣāra‘ath have continued to be applied to sufferers from mycobacterial leprosy.

MYCOBACTERIAL LEPROSY

Mycobacterial leprosy results from an infection with *Mycobacterium leprae* discovered in 1874 by Hansen.[8] The major obstacle in the study of leprosy was that *M. leprae* only grows intracellularly and then only very slowly needing twelve days or more to replicate. However, within the last two decades, important advances have been made, *M. leprae* can now be maintained in the pad of a mouse's foot and more recently it has been found that *M. leprae* can also be grown in large numbers in the nine-banded armadillo and even more recently in vervet monkeys.

The tissues respond to the invasion of cells by *M. leprae* by the collection of scavenger cells (macrophages) around the areas of infection. *M. leprae* has a special affinity for nerves and the skin though all organs may be, and are, infected. Diagnosis nowadays is confirmed by smears taken from incisions in the skin. Under standardised conditions the number of bacilli present in the smear has prognostic significance.

Most adults are immune to infection by *M. leprae*, so much so that until recently it was thought that adults did not contract leprosy in spite of close contact (e.g. nuns or nurses in a leprosarium). A small number of adults may become infected, displaying faint patches of discoloration of the skin known as indeterminate leprosy. Most (70 per cent or more) develop adequate cellular response to overcome the infection and recover. A few may proceed to overt disease which shows itself in two forms, tuberculoid and lepromatous. In the tuberculoid form the body's resistance is strong and skin lesions are localised to raised convex plaques. Few bacilli are present in the skin and risk of transmission is small. Especially important, however, is the compression of the nerves by an exaggerated tissue response and the consequent loss of sensation and trophic effects. In lepromatous leprosy, the tissues have little resistance; florid, diffuse and spreading thickening of the skin occurs. Vast numbers of bacilli are present in the skin and as these are shed this form is more infectious. The skin of the face becomes shiny and swollen, giving rise to the leonine facies, the eyebrows fall out (otherwise the hair is not affected), the ears and the nose are swollen, nasal discharges are excessive and blindness due to inflammation of the cornea (keratitis) ensues. In both forms of leprosy skin lesions have a reddish tinge and though, later, depigmentation may occur, this is not a striking feature. Again in both forms the lesions are dry and shiny rather than overtly scaly. As might be expected, most cases fall between the two poles of tuberculoid and lepromatous presentations. These are known as borderline.

Untreated leprosy is inexorably progressive, the rate of progression depending on how immunity develops. Towards the end of life the disease often appears to be burnt out and further progression is slow. Its spread through the community, both by its development in an individual and by the nature of its transmission, is also slow. Leprosy is not highly infective. It is a remarkable fact that fewer than 5 per cent of spouses contract leprosy from an infected partner. The relative immunity of adults means that unless children, who have little immunity, are present (and they will not show the disease for ten or more years) leprosy will spread even more slowly. This makes epidemiological studies difficult. Congenital transmission does not occur. With modern treatment the chances of a cure are good, and drug regimes allow a patient to be returned to the community with safety. There is now every prospect of the development of a vaccine.

M. *leprae* is closely related to *Mycobacterium tuberculae*, the organism of tuberculosis, but there is little cross-immunity. Both infections may be present in the same person. Vaccination with BCG (Bacillus Calmette Guérin) against tuberculosis does not seem very effective against leprosy; at best about 30 per cent of persons derive some protection.

MYCOBACTERIAL LEPROSY IN PALESTINE

It is not known for certain how mycobacterial leprosy reached the Eastern Mediterranean but the most attractive theory is that it was introduced by the armies of Alexander the Great when they returned from campaigning in northern India, where the disease was prevalent, in 324–322 BC[9] (see Table 2). After Alexander's death in 323 BC and the wars which followed the division of his empire, some of his soldiers with their Asian wives and children settled in Palestine in a confederation of Greek cities which came to be known as the Decapolis. All the cities of the Decapolis, with the exception of Scythopolis, were east of the Jordan. But the long incubation period, two to ten years or more, the fact that the spread of the disease is dependent on the

Table 2. Mycobacterial leprosy: important dates

Date	
600 BC	Written evidence of M. leprosy in India (the Sanskrit medical treatises *Susrutha Samhita*[6])
500–200 BC	References to M. leprosy in Chinese literature (the medical classic. *Nei Ching Su Wen*[6])
587–538 BC	Jewish exile in Babylon. Latest date for final redaction of Leviticus
460–370 BC	Hippocratic writings use plural *leprae* to refer to variety of skin ailments
327–323 BC	Return of Alexander the Great's armies from India, accompanied by Asian wives and children
c. 200 BC	References in Greek literature to a new disease which was named *elephantiasis graecorum*
First to fourth centuries AD	The terms *lepra* and *elephantiasis graecorum* were both used to describe M. leprosy. Gradually *lepra* alone was used and *elephantiasis* applied to another disease.

presence of children, and the circumscribed area in which the soldiers and their families settled, mean that the disease was unlikely to spread quickly throughout the country. Whether the lepers met by Christ were suffering from mycobacterial leprosy is not known, but on a geographical and statistical basis the chances are low.

AS SNOW

Apart from Moses, whose hand is described as leprous when the Lord taught him a trick (see page 27), four persons are mentioned in the Old Testament as being afflicted with ṣāra'ath: Miriam, King Uzziah, Naaman and Gehazi. The leprosy of Moses's hand (Exodus 4:6), that of Miriam (Numbers 12:10) and that of Gehazi (II Kings 5:27) are described as being 'white as snow'. The epithet 'white' first appears in the Vulgate, Jerome's translation; the Hebrew Scriptures merely refer to ṣāraʿath being 'as snow'. Hulse[10] argues that the original description 'as snow' refers to the desquamating character of the lesions. For this reason he suggests that the desquamating diseases – psoriasis, pityriasis rosea, seborrhoeic dermatitis, patchy eczema and favus – all of which may have a high psychic content in their cause, might be the equivalent of ṣāraʿath.

Miriam is said to have been punished by the Lord for criticising Moses. Aaron's plea that Miriam should not be like the flesh of a still-born child gives some credence to the scaliness of her lesions (Numbers 12:12). She was expelled from the camp for seven days but she did not undergo any purification rite or offer any sacrifices when she came back. The most likely diagnosis of her ṣāraʿath is desquamation of the skin after scarlet fever or similar infection (see page 76).

King Uzziah (II Chronicles 26:16–21) usurped the prerogative of the priests and burned incense to the Lord. When the High Priest and his coterie of eighty priests interfered, he grew angry and ṣāraʿath broke out on his forehead. As a result he had to give up his official duties and live in a separate house for the rest of his life. By implication the onset of his ṣāraʿath was sudden. It did not remit because, doubtless, the priests saw to it that he was not allowed to forget his sin and so he did not achieve psychological calm.

NAAMAN

Naaman, a Syrian, the commander of the armies of the King of Syria, decided, on the suggestion of his wife's maid who had been captured in a recent raid on Samaria, to consult Elisha about a cure for his ṣāraʿath (II Kings 5). Almost certainly Naaman travelled to Samaria by the King's Highway, a fortified and patrolled road in safe territory east of the Jordan. He crossed the Jordan at the confluence with the Jabbok and proceeded with his chariots and his horses through potentially hostile country to Samaria. After presenting his diplomatic letters of credence to the King of Israel, who was greatly alarmed at his arrival, he went to see Elisha. Elisha caused him much annoyance by his casual reception, and the prescription to bathe seven times in the muddy waters of the Jordan seemed absurd. After an argument with his servants about whether to act on Elisha's advice, Naaman dipped in the Jordan and was cured. Elisha would not accept any reward from Naaman, but his servant Gehazi was greedy and tricked Naaman into giving him silver and festal garments. On being rebuked by Elisha, Gehazi developed *ṣāra'ath*, again of sudden onset, doubtless brought on by the anxiety of guilt.

As Naaman was not an Israelite his *ṣāra'ath* did not make him ritually unclean, but it must have been very worrying to him and lasted a long time to justify such a journey. Getting ready would have required considerable effort, and leaving home and travelling to a hostile country where he was unsure of his reception would have been distressing and worrying. Then during the journey there would have been the anticipatory excitement of a cure. This would have been followed by his anger at the unexpected advice of Elisha, his dispute with his servants and finally his acceptance of Elisha's instructions. All these elements would result in a high degree of tension. Dipping in the Jordan was the nostrum to which the cure of his dermatitis was ascribed, but it was, in reality, the signal for discharge of emotion.

Browne[11] suggests that Naaman's *ṣāra'ath* was really scabies, which could have been cured by dipping in the sulphur springs of Rabbi Mayer near Tiberias. This seems unlikely. Naaman was a high-ranking officer and once he had decided to accept Elisha's advice about washing in the Jordan it is most improbable that he would ignore his instructions, especially as they had been given to him in front of his servants, or that he would mistake the Jordan for the springs of Rabbi Mayer. The springs to which Browne refers are the hot springs south of Tiberias, near the tomb of Rabbi Me'ir Ba'al HaNess. They are not sulphurous* as a visit can confirm.

There are two other reasons why Naaman did not suffer from scabies. First, scabies is transmitted by skin to skin contact under conditions warm enough to make the *Acarus scabei* thoroughly motile. The parts of the body most likely to harbour the mites are the hands, wrists and elbows.[17,18] Yet the King of Syria did not contract scabies though he regularly leaned on Naaman's arm on his way to worship in the House of Rimmon. Secondly, scabies is not transmitted by clothes or other fomites. During the Second World War, when the control of scabies was especially important, a number of volunteers slept in beds immediately after they had been vacated by persons heavily infected with scabies. They did not contract scabies. In other experiments towels used by many hundreds of cases of scabies were later used again by uninfected volunteers without a single instance of transmission.[17,18] This disposes of the suggestion that Naaman had scabies and that Gehazi caught it from the garments which he had wrongfully acquired from Naaman.

An essential prerequisite for the relief of neuro-dermatitis is psychic calm. Naaman underwent a formal abreaction[19] or working through emotional tension. For less severe cases

---

*Browne appears to have been misled by an anonymous editorial published in 1938 in the *Leprosy Review*[12] in which the writer recollects that thirty-five years previously the Arabs dipped in the springs of Rabbi Mayer, which he says were sulphurous, and that as a result of this they rarely attended hospital for the treatment of scabies. Smith[13] states that the spring waters contain calcium carbonate and a small proportion of muriatic (hydrochloric) salts. Morton[14] states that the springs are like those at Carlsbad, which means that the waters contain sodium sulphate and sodium carbonate. The fact that the springs are not sulphurous has been confirmed by Oren[15] and by the Embassy of Israel in London.[16]

age-old methods may have been sufficient; rest, removal from stress (including domestic stress), sympathetic listening and alcohol (see page 246).

JESUS AND THE LEPERS

The incident of the cleansing of the ten lepers by Jesus described in Luke (17:12–19) is an example of the sudden relief of nervous tension and its effect on a nervously induced or maintained skin condition. In such cases instantaneous relief of the skin lesions would rarely occur, but the cure would start very quickly and it would become obvious that it was starting within a very short time, possibly in minutes and certainly in hours. That is exactly what Luke reports. When the ten lepers left Jesus they were undoubtedly in an ecstatically relaxed frame of mind. Luke does not report an immediate cure but says that 'as they went they were cleansed' and it was not until some time after that one returned to give thanks for the cure.

Mark (1:40–45), Matthew (8:1–4) and Luke (5:12–16) all tell the story of the one leper who was touched by Jesus undergoing immediate cure. It is extremely reasonable that neuro-dermatitis would in the extreme ecstasy of being touched by Jesus – a sign that the leper is accepted, indeed loved, by the Messiah – show visible improvement very quickly indeed. When the leper was touched, the overwhelming psychic energy of ecstasy displaced that of anxiety.

SACRIFICES

The laws governing sacrificial offerings appear in two contrasting forms. In Chapters 1–6:7 the ritual prescriptions are described from the standpoint of the person making the offering, whereas in Chapters 6:8–7:36 the narrative considers the various sacrifices as the priests had to deal with them. The proper animals for sacrifice vary both according to the type of sacrifice and social status of the supplicant. If a man cannot afford more he may sacrifice two turtle doves or pigeons, and, if he cannot afford these, he has to sacrifice a tenth of an ephah of fine flour. An ephah varied from 4½ to 9 gallons (20.5 to 41 litres). Certainly for the poor (and possibly for the nation as a whole) such frequent and costly sacrifices raise the question of how much the food intake was diminished. The priest did quite well as the breast and the right thigh of the animals were reserved for him. The right thigh was considered one of the choicest parts of the animal. In I Samuel (9:24) it was the portion reserved for the guest of honour.

The technical difficulties of sacrifice must have been considerable; slaughtering the animal, draining it of blood (4:30) and incinerating the whole or part. Cremation of a human corpse is usually undertaken at a temperature of 2000°C if in a coffin, and 1800°C if not in a coffin. Even if only part of the animal was burned, some being reserved for the priests and some for the offerer, a high temperature had to be reached. When the flesh was consumed by fire, the bones would be more or less intact. Wood (1:7) seems to have been the source of the fire.[20] The Chinese, around 2000–1700 BC, attained temperatures of 1050°C in melting bronze and brass[21] using charcoal. Solomon had an export business in copper and iron. His technicians must have been able to attain these temperatures to smelt ore from the mines (where the price of Solomon's glory was at best the hope of a quick death). At Ezion-Geber tunnels were arranged so as to use the prevailing wind as a forced draught.[1] No such arrangement existed in temples, and a temperature of 400°C is likely to have been the highest that could be reached. Because of its water content wood burns at a lower temperature than charcoal. Making the fire bigger (to avoid cooling at its edges) and the use of bellows (none appears to have been used) would raise the temperature.

Even so, the sacrifice must have been a troublesome, not to say messy, business, especially as the priests had to throw the blood around the altar. Directions about how blood should be scattered on the altar and its base are given (1:5), and instructions as to when the altar and its base should be cleansed. How this was to be done is not stated. Slaughter was daily. The odour of the burning flesh and fat would scarcely have been pleasing to the Lord (2:2, Exodus 29:41).

In spite of instructions to burn the remains and any dung outside the camp (Exodus 29:14), to wonder about the hygiene and cleanliness of the Temple is not unreasonable. Lack of precise instructions about hygiene is in contrast to the required washing of the priests (16:4), exclusion of sick persons (21:18), blemished animals (22:20) and the requirement to keep the camp clean (Deuteronomy 23:14).

Chapters 40–43 of Ezekiel give a description of his dream Temple (see page 180). It was 292 yards (267 m) square and the altar, which appears to have been among the largest,[20] had an uppermost level of 18 feet (5.5 m) square. Close to the east entrance eight tables were provided so that on these animals could be bled to death. Over the tables there were hooks on which to hang meat. Lofthouse[22] reduces these descriptions and measurements to a plan.

It is difficult to avoid the conclusion that the Temple was a cross between an abattoir and a fly-ridden old-fashioned butcher's shop. The only difference is that the animals were not stunned before having their throats slit to bleed slowly to death. This, of course, has to be seen against a secular background of overcrowded housing conditions, poor ventilation, dirt and dust, and unwashed bodies due to a scarcity of water.

DIETARY PROHIBITIONS

Leviticus 3:17 states: 'It shall be a perpetual statute through-out your generations, in all your dwelling places, that you eat neither fat nor blood.' The ban on fat was because it was regarded as a particularly choice portion of the sacrifice and therefore the perquisite of the Lord. The prohibition on eating blood, which is reiterated in Deuteronomy 12:16,23, arose because blood was the seat of life (17:11) and since life was the property and gift of God it had to be returned to him and not appropriated by human beings (see page 91). A further general prohibition is the ban on eating any animal that dies of itself or is killed by wild beasts (17:15).

Table 3. Kosher and non-kosher foods

Leviticus – Chapter 11	Deuteronomy – Chapter 14

1. **Animals**
   Animals which part the hoof and are cloven footed and chew the cut may be eaten

	Oxen, Wild goat Sheep, Ibex Goat Hart, Antelope Gazelle, Mountain- sheep Roebuck ⎫ permitted

Camel ⎫ prohibited
Rock badger* ⎬ as not
Hare ⎭ cloven footed
Swine – prohibited as do
  not chew the cud
	Camel ⎫ Prohibited
	Rock badger ⎬ as not
	Hare ⎭ cloven footed
	Swine – prohibited as do
	  not chew the cud

*Rock badger (hydrax) of similar size and appearance to a rabbit or a cat but probably related to the rhinoceros. Grass eating, now only extant on Table Mountain, Cape Province, South Africa, where it is called dassie. Genus hydrax difficult to classify.

Table 3 (cont.)

2. **Fish and other sea creatures**

    All those with fins and scales may be eaten, but those without
    fins and scales are prohibited.

3. **Birds**

All may be eaten except eagle, vulture, osprey, kite, falcon, raven, ostrich, nighthawk, seagull, hawk, owl, cormorant, ibis, water hen, pelican, carrion vulture, stork, heron, hoopoe and the bat [*sic*]	All may be eaten except eagle, vulture, osprey, buzzard, kite, raven, ostrich, nighthawk, seagull, hawk, little owl, great owl, water hen, pelican, carrion vulture, cormorant, stork, heron, hoopoe and the bat [*sic*]

4. **Insects**

All winged insects that go on all fours prohibited except locust, bald locust, cricket and grasshopper. These are permitted because they hop along the ground.	All winged insects prohibited

5. **Animals that go on their paws**
    These must not be eaten.
    The Hebrew *kaph*, translated as
    paws means palm of the hand.
    This prohibition is thought to
    refer to cats and dogs

6. **Swarming things on the earth**
    Weasel, mouse, great lizard,
    gecko, land crocodile[5], lizard,
    sand lizard and chameleon are
    prohibited

[5]This is thought to be a tortoise or a kind of lizard.

Table 3 (cont.)

7.	**Swarming things that go on their belly, on all fours, or have many feet** These may not be eaten. This prohibition is thought to refer to snakes, lizards, worms, caterpillars, centipedes etc.

In addition to these general prohibitions both Leviticus and Deuteronomy lay down detailed guidelines as to what food is clean and may be eaten and what food is unclean and therefore may not be eaten. These prohibitions, which are summarised in Table 3, have no justification either nutritionally or medically. The word 'kosher' which is applied nowadays to Jewish food derives from the Hebrew *kosher* meaning right or proper.

The lack of protest (if correctly reported) suggests that these prohibitions were already customary before they were promulgated. Moses's enthusiastic endorsement of these customs is likely to have had as much to do with securing his Pharaonic dictatorship as anything else.

What is acceptable food is culturally determined; the eating of horseflesh is questioned in Britain, but in France is acceptable. Insects are regularly eaten by Australian aborigines, rats' legs and day-old mice in Borneo. Camel meat is a delicacy to Arabs, and dried locusts were to small boys in England in the inter-war years. Dogs die a painful death to provide meat which is thought to be a delicacy in Korea. Once established such mores are very strong.

Pigs, one of the species declared unclean, are omnivores and in particular root for tubers. In the context of semi-desert farming, pigs are direct competitors with man for their food. Pigs are sensitive to heat and sunlight and to keep cool, which they must, they wallow in mud and faeces. Ritual prohibition against eating pork is much more likely to have arisen from these two reasons than from any consideration of health. Maimonides[23] (AD 1135–1204) argued that, while he could find hygienic reasons for all the other dietary restrictions of the Mosaic law, he was baffled by the prohibition on pork and finally decided: 'The principal reason why the Lord forbids swine's flesh is to be found in the circumstance that its habits and its foods are very dirty and loathsome.'

Eating 'measly pork' may cause severe pain due to larvae of *Trichinella spiralis* being deposited in the muscles. Well-cooked pork is free from risk. The condition is self-limiting, usually within a few weeks after the larvae have encysted. Compared with tapeworm (*Taenia solium*), also spread by pigs, and which may have severe nutritional and medical consequences, infection with *Trichinella spiralis*, though very painful, is comparatively unimportant. The ban against eating pig was based on ritual grounds and not on logic; if hygiene was the reason, the eating of the flesh of other animals should also have been proscribed.

The Jewish attitude to the pig may have arisen from the ancient West Semitic attitude which dates back to pre-Israelite times. De Vaux[24] points out that in West Semitic culture the pig was not normally sacrificed or eaten. It was regarded as a demoniacal animal in contact with the gods of the under-world and was sacrificed to those gods in certain secret rites which took place only rarely. In Palestine the bones of pigs have been found in underground sanctuaries to enable the sacrificed animals to be nearer the gods of the underworld. In Greece, at the great feast of Demeter and Persephone, live piglets were thrown into ditches and were thus despatched to hell. In Cyprus, pigs were sacrificed to Aphrodite once a year on the second day of April. Herodotus[25] reports that the Egyptians considered it proper to sacrifice pigs only to Dionysus and to the Moon. To both these deities they offered pigs once a year. After the sacrifice the meat was eaten, but on no other day did the Egyptians touch it. Plutarch[26] says that the Egyptians held the pig to be unclean because it was inclined to mate at the waning of the moon and because the bodies of those who drank its milk break out with leprosy and scabrous itching.

During the attempt by Antiochus Epiphanes (175 – 163 BC) to Hellenise the Jewish nation, Jews were ordered to eat swine's flesh on pain of death; many refused and were martyred.[27] Finally, the cult of Zeus was introduced into the Temple at Jerusalem and swine's flesh was offered upon the altar. There followed the Maccabean rebellion[27] (see page 193).

Oxen and cows are not prohibited foods. Besides being the source of *Taenia saginata* (another tapeworm) they also cause infection with tuberculosis, usually of the gut, kidney and bone. Camels, rodents, deer, pigs, cattle and particularly sheep may be the intermediate host of *Echinococcus granulosus*. The life cycle includes dogs who may spread the disease to man. Symptoms are due to cysts in various organs and in the brain the space occupying lesion may manifest as epilepsy. The disease is present in the Middle East today, though it is especially important in Australia, New Zealand and Iceland. Some 10 per cent of sheepdogs may be infected. Fish from the Mediterranean or the Sea of Galilee are most unlikely to have been the source of other tapeworms (*Dibrothriocephalus latus*).

Possibly more important worm infections than those so far described are hookworms (*Ankylostoma duodenale*), round worms (*Ascaris lumbricoides* and *Strongyloides stercoralis*). Such worms would be a major hazard in nomadic life where people went from waterhole to waterhole, with bare feet or very lightly shod, accompanied by near-naked children. The eggs of the first two are passed in faeces and develop into larvae in moist soil. The dry dust of the desert would be lethal to the larvae, but there would have been sufficient wet soil around well-heads to ensure propagation. The larvae penetrate the skin and through the bloodstream reach the gut, or they may be (possibly more often) swallowed in water or by eating contaminated vegetables. Hookworm sucks blood and will cause severe anaemia and protein loss. Death may occur especially in children in the absence of treatment (and some persons say even with treatment). The best thing to do is to live longer than five years without reinfection, as this is the life span of the worm. Vast, almost astronomical, numbers of round worm may develop in the gut causing distension of the gut and consequently of the abdomen by the space they occupy. Even with relatively few worms nutrition of children is severely affected. *Strongyloides* may complete its life cycle within the gut, though contact with stools may perpetuate the infection. Subcutaneous migration of the larvae is not uncommon.

Nowhere is there any record of the Israelites being affected by these (or other) parasites. However, living as they did it was almost inevitable that they were heavily infected. Confirmation of this view is provided by the recent work of the Manchester Egyptian Mummy Project.[28] Besides discovering evidence of *Taenia, Trichinella, Echinococcus* and *Ankylostoma* infection, one out of the five mummies examined showed *Dracunculus medinensis* (guinea worm) (see page 81).

UNCLEANNESS; VENEREAL DISEASE

Uncleanness raises its guilty head in verse 7:19 as it does recurrently throughout Leviticus, particularly in relation to leprosy. The ascription of uncleanness after childbirth (12:2) might have been protective of the woman and a not entirely reliable form of birth control. The period of uncleanness after childbirth varies from forty days if the baby was a boy to eighty days if the baby was a girl. During that time the mother must not touch any hallowed thing or enter the sanctuary. At the end of her period of uncleanness she must make an offering of a lamb and two turtle doves or two pigeons. Here it is interesting to note that the likelihood of conception is highest in the middle of the menstrual cycle. Some evidence exists that boys are more likely to be conceived early in the menstrual cycle, hence the increase in male births after a war partly, but not entirely, due to the eager activities of returning soldiers.

Chapter 15 opens with a discussion of the uncleanness of a man with a discharge from his genital organs. Many of the discharges described in verses 15:2ff. were due to gonorrhoeal urethritis following impure intercourse. Gonorrhoeal urethritis unless treated (and effective treatment was not available to the Israelites) nearly always becomes chronic and in men may well result in a stricture. As this narrows the urethra progressive difficulties would be experienced in passing urine, with increasing back pressure on the bladder, ureters and kidneys. Death from uraemia would follow fairly soon. The list of prohibitions, briefly any bed or object on which the sufferer has sat and his body and clothes, associated with such uncleanness would provide a salutary lesson for others, but since *Neisseria gonorrhoae* (the bacteria which causes gonorrhoea) does not survive for long out of the body, especially when dry, they would have minor preventive effect, except perhaps as regards the eyes of newly born children. Gonorrhoeal conjunctivitis, by denuding the cornea epithelium, results in blindness. Gonococcal infections of the eye in the form of ophthalmia neonatorum acquired during birth, account for some 90 per cent of children said to have been born blind. Other causes of urethral infections with the consequent discharge are *E. coli* urethritis in older men and homosexual practices (see page 14) and the experimental introduction of foreign bodies (even a clinical thermometer by a medical student after taking his rectal temperature).

Common decency to menstruating women seems to have been promoted to a ritual prohibition of intercourse during menstruation (15:19) when it would not lead to conception. Menorrhagia (15:25), uterine loss of blood other than during menstruation, may, though not always, be chronic and very debilitating. The uncleanness of menstruation and menorrhagia again shows the fear of blood. The penalties laid on women for intercourse during menstruation are again greater than those incurred by men. Involuntary discharge of semen (15:32) is harmless (and possibly pleasurable); again uncleanness is the result.

ILLNESS AND PUNISHMENT

Illness was thought to be a punishment sent by the Lord for acts offensive to him. Such an idea is perpetuated from prehistoric times. Man likes to have an explanation even when living as not much more than the victim of natural forces. He may have felt guilty at not observing, even if unknowingly, the Lord's requirements, but what good came of the cruel and messy sacrifices of animals is difficult for the modern mind to comprehend. As an example ṣāra'ath might as well be ascribed to the Lord's displeasure as to anything else known to Moses. For a race so obsessed with tribal ties, a curious fact is that they appeared to have so little understanding of the psyche. Guilt, that is anxiety at the failure or inability to meet a prescribed standard of behaviour, surrounded every part of their living. When to standards prescribed by the Lord (the Ten Commandments contain the essential precepts of morality and religion) are added trivialities (19:19), no wonder anxiety was common.

SEXUAL RELATIONS AND OTHER PROHIBITIONS

In their incest, Lot's daughters (see page 11) did not break the table of affinity (18:6ff.) if they had known of it, but they evaded its intention. The table is all good sense as consanguineous marriages increase the chance of persons liable to transmit congenital disease marrying each other. Congenital disease among the progeny of marriages between two such persons will still be rare, but not quite as rare if mating took place at random. Chapters 18 and 20 deal with various aspects of moral purity and the consequences of not obeying the law. They list a series of sexual crimes for which the punishment is death. These include incestuous relationships within a wide family circle, homosexuality by men and bestiality by both men and women. To these have been added various provisions including the prohibition of child sacrifice to pagan gods.

Chapter 19 covers a number of miscellaneous regulations aimed at enhancing the holiness and purity of the people of Israel by observing the principle of separateness. The breeding of different kinds of cattle to produce hybrid species is forbidden, a field must not be sown with two kinds of seed, nor shall a garment be made of two different types of material. In the moral realm, a man who has intercourse with a slave betrothed to another man has to make a guilt offering to atone for his sin and a man must not make his daughter a prostitute. To keep stock, including human stock, pure is a continuing concept. In AD 1300 the Abbess of Chatteris[29] fined Rosea, daughter of Matilda Lawe, twelve pence for committing lethewyte (intercourse with a bondsman) and Richard Legat forty pence for fornicating with a kinswoman, whereas the usual rate of fines for fornication was between three pence and six pence. The Race Relations Act 1976, which requires that strangers are treated as equals, is foreshadowed (19:33).

The Israelites were to avoid shaving the hair of the temples, trimming their beards and being tattooed (19:27, 28). The introduction of dyes under the skin may itself cause inflammatory reaction, but today, unless care is taken to ensure that needles are sterile, syphilis, hepatitis-B and HIV may be inoculated. Persons seeking to be tattooed are said, for uncertain reasons, to have a lascivious character, especially if they are women.

The Lord's injunction in the wonderful passage 'love your neighbour as yourself' (19:18), the exhortation to be kind to the deaf and blind (19:14), and the prohibition of lying and of witchcraft (19:16, 26, 31) lie incongruously with the other sins and their prescribed penalties.

PHYSICAL DEFECTS AND BLEMISHES

Both the priest and the sacrificial animal he offers must be free from physical blemishes (see page 56). The imperfections listed include blindness, facial mutilation (a split nose), sight defects, limbs of uneven length, hunchback and itching diseases of various kinds (21:17–21). No doubt this is the obverse of the argument that only the most valued should be offered to the Lord and, of course, the first born are the most valuable (Numbers 18:15; Deuteronomy 12:17, 15:19). Abraham's uncompleted sacrifice of Isaac may have had similar motivation.

The likely cause of blindness depends on the age of the propitus. In childhood, xerophthalmia due to deficiency of vitamin A would not occur in a pastoral people (though it has been common until recently in the Third World due to deficiency in artificial milk powder). Corneal scarring following specific fevers, such as smallpox and measles and trachoma (spread by flies), would be prevalent. In adolescence and in young adults injury would be an important cause. In later life, glaucoma, diabetic retinitis and cataract may all, in the absence of treatment, proceed to blindness.

The Hebrew *ḥārem* (21:18) means a split nose, which suggests that the nostrils were separated. Injury might achieve this, but so would disease of the nasal septum. Today congenital syphilis leading to 'saddle nose', very largely due to destruction of the septum, would be regarded as the major cause of such deformity, but syphilis was not imported from the New World until about 1495 (see page 97). Saddle nose may also occur in achondroplasia. Mycobacterial leprosy, in its lepromatous form, will destroy the cartilaginous part of the nasal septum. Again, it was not present in Israel until after Leviticus had been reduced to its final form (see page 46). Another cause of the destruction of the septum is *lupus erythematosis*. This is an auto-immune disease related in an ill-understood way to *systemic lupus erythematosis*, which is an immune disease of major gravity affecting all the connective tissue including that in joints, pleura, pericardium, heart and kidney. In *lupus erythematosis* a scaly and disfiguring rash affects the face and often the other parts of the skin exposed to sunlight.

The Hebrew *ḥārem* is derived from the verb *ḥāram*, which is capable of meaning to split the soft tissues in the nasal part of the maxilla. A hare lip and cleft palate (both of congenital origin) would qualify for inclusion.

The obvious cause of hunchback is collapse of a vertebra due to bone tuberculosis, which must have been common considering the prevalence of bovine (and human) tuberculosis. Osteoporosis (in the aged) and ankylosing spondylitis would also cause forward bending. Shortening of the limbs would occur as the aftermath of poliomyelitis, which is likely to have been very frequent, or of fractures. Hands and arms may be affected for the same reasons, to which must be added injuries of the brachial plexus. Very short limbs occur in achondroplasia (a familial disease) and in various endocrine diseases such as hypothyroidism and deficiency of growth hormone.

Just about any skin disease is covered by verse 21:20. The Hebrew *yallepheth* means a disease with a scab or eruption, and *gārābh* means a disease with an itch, scab or festering sore. Scabies is high on the list for inclusion. Perhaps it is worth mentioning here that scabies is no no respecter of persons or social class. As was said on page 55 scabies is spread by skin to skin contact. Persons living in overcrowded conditions are more likely to catch it and they are likely to be dirtier. The burrows of the *Sarcoptes acarus scabei* are more easily seen if dirt is rubbed into them. Diagnosis in clean people can be puzzling.

Also barred (21:20) from offering sacrifices was a person suffering from *mᵉrôah*. This Hebrew word means either rubbing away or enlargement of the testicles (see page 93).

Many more serious diseases, of which the Israelites must have been aware, even in the absence of precise means of diagnosis, are not proscribed. For example, goitre, acromegaly and neuro-fibromatosis, all of which are disfiguring diseases. However, in the next chapter (22:4) priests suffering from *ṣāra'ath*, with a discharge (even if only semen), or who have touched unclean things, are barred both from officiating at a sacrifice and from eating priestly food. The ritual complications are enormous and further elaborated in 22:10ff. Unless we assume that the Hebrews had realised, unlike Pharaoh, that the size of future population, whether men, cattle, sheep or goats, depends on the number of females capable of breeding, masculinity is emphasised (22:19, 23:12, 18, 19) by requiring sacrifices to be of male animals. The final insult is reached (27:4) when valuation of a male is twice or nearly so that of a female.

The burning fever (*qadaḥath*) and wasting disease (*šaḥepheth*) mentioned in verse 26:16 may be tuberculosis or alternatively exophthalmic goitre (hyperthyroidism). They are part of a lengthy curse which, if it became operative, would leave very little on earth.

References

1. Wright G.E. *Biblical Archaeology*. London: Duckworth, 1962.
2. Martindale W., Westcott W.W. *The Extra Pharmacopoeia*, 24th edn., ed. Reynolds J.E.F., London: Pharmaceutical Press, 1958.
3. Plato. *The Last Days of Socrates*, trans. Tredennick H., Harmondsworth: Penguin Books, 1964.
4. Dreisback R.H. *Poisoning*. Los Altos, California: Lange Medical Publications, 1966.
5. Charles R.H. *The Apocrypha and Pseudepigrapha of the Old Testament*, Vol. II. Oxford: Clarendon Press, 1913.
6. Lloyd Davies M. Leprosy and Leviticus: Uncleanness and the Psyche. Oxford: Pusey House Library. (Thesis awarded S.Th. (Lambeth) 1986.)
7. Lloyd Davies M. Levitical leprosy: uncleanness and the psyche. *Expository Times*. 1988, *99*: 136.
8. Hansen G.A. trans. anon. *International Journal of Leprosy*. 1878, *23*: 207.
9. Lane Fox R. *Alexander the Great*. London: Allen Lane, 1973.
10. Hulse E.V. The Nature of Biblical Leprosy and the Use of Alternative Medical Terms in Modern Translations of the Bible. *Palestine Exploration Quarterly*. 1975, *107*: 87.
11. Browne S.G. *Leprosy in the Bible*. London: Christian Medical Fellowship, 1979.
12. Anon. Editorial. *Leprosy Review*. 1938, *9*: 48.
13. Smith G.A. *The Historical Geography of the Holy Land*. London: Collins (Fontana Library of Theology), 1966.
14. Morton H.V. *In the Steps of the Master*. London: Rich & Cowan, 1934.
15. Oren O.H. Physical and Chemical Characteristics of Lake Tiberias. *Bulletin of the Research Council of Israel*. 1962, 11G, 1.
16. Rosen E. Counsellor, Cultural Affairs, Embassy of Israel, London – private communication, 1984.
17. Mellanby K. *Scabies* (Oxford War Manuals). London: Oxford University Press, 1943.

18. Mellanby K. *Scabies*. Hampton, Middlesex: E.W. Classey, 1972.

19. Sargant W. *Battle for the Mind: A Physiology of Conversion and Brainwashing*. London: Heinemann, 1957.

20. Gray C.B. *Sacrifice in the Old Testament*. Oxford: Oxford University Press, 1925.

21. Tylecote R.F. Ancient metallurgy in China. *Technologist*. Sept. 1983, 435.

22. Lofthouse W.F. *Israel after the Exile*. Oxford: Clarendon Press, 1928.

23. Maimonides. *The Guide for the Perplexed*, trans. Friedlander M., London: Routledge, 1928.

24. De Vaux R. *The Bible and the Ancient Near East*. London: Darton, Longman & Todd, 1972.

25. Herodotus. *The Histories,* trans. Aubrey de Selincourt. Harmondsworth: Penguin Books, 1983.

26. Plutarch. Isis and Osiris. *Moralia*. Loeb Classical Library. London: Heinemann, 1969.

27. I and II Maccabees. The Apocrypha, Revised Standard Version. New York: Oxford University Press, 1957.

28. David R., Tapp E. *Evidence Embalmed*. Manchester: Manchester University Press, 1984.

29. Parker R. *The Common Stream*. St Albans: Paladin, 1976.

NUMBERS

CENSUS

The object of Moses's census (1:2) was to find out how many males of 20 years and upwards were able to go to war (1:3). Excluding the tribe of Levi,* who were the priests (1:49), the total was 603,550 men (1:46). The position of women is not clear. This total is not unlike the 600,000 men said to have taken part in the Exodus (Exodus 12:37).

HEALTH

The deaths of Nadab and Abihu (3:4) are discussed on page 42. The Lord (or Moses) in expelling from the camp lepers, persons with a discharge or those who had had contact with the dead was concerned with ritual cleanness, rather than health (5:2).

INDIGNITY TO WOMEN

If any excuse for feminism is needed, this is it (5:14). The poor woman who has not been unfaithful to her husband

---

*The tribe of Levi numbered 22,300 (3:22, 28, 34)

is subject to indignities before the priest on the basis only of her husband's jealous imaginings that she may have gone astray. 'The man shall be free from iniquity but the woman shall bear her iniquity' (5:31). Surely there could not have been, or could never be, a more degrading form of sex-based servitude. Perhaps the Israelite society of that time was more like that described by Zuckerman[1] in which the fight between males to possess females introduced into a colony of monkeys or apes ends in the death of the females.

ANATOMICAL KNOWLEDGE

The Israelite's knowledge of anatomy was limited. The acquisition of uncleanness by touching a dead body* precluded dissection. The number of bones in the body was thought to be 248, but this figure was derived from the numerical value assigned to the letters in Abraham's name.[2] The Israelites did not distinguish between bones and joints. The number of bones in the human body is 206; the definition of joints is imprecise, but these number upwards of 275.

PRIESTS

There is some suggestion that priests were grossly overfed and very well rewarded. Unlike their congregation they had a fixed retiring age of 50 years (8:25). To make sure that

---

*In the parable of the good Samaritan (Luke 10:30–37) it could be that the priest and the Levite passed by on the other side because they feared that the man who had been left by the thieves was either dead or might die as they tended him. They would then be unclean and unfit for their Temple duties (Leviticus 22:3).

they did so they had to attend the services but perform
minor duties only.

LIFE IN THE DESERT: MANNA AND QUAILS

Though the march order seems to have been laid down for
the Israelites, the arrangements for food, water and latrines
seem to have been beneath mention. When they reached
Taberah (in the Sinai Peninsula) the Israelites complained
of their misfortunes (11:1), and even more when the camp
was burnt. For the second time manna (11:7), the extruded
sap of the *Tamarix gallica*, sustained them (see page 36).
In spite of the manna the people demanded meat (11:4)
and the Lord, instigated by Moses, pronounced that the
people, numbering 600,000 (11:21), should have meat, a
promise very conveniently met when flocks of quails were
blown down near the camp (11:31). Quails, in spite of their
small size, are powerful flyers over short distances but may
be blown down by the wind. They were at a height of two
cubits, about 3 feet 8 inches (1.1 m) and so an easy prey.
The least greedy man is said to have gathered ten homers
of quails and as a homer is the size of a tea-chest a vast
number must have been caught. The result of this gluttony
was mass poisoning, resulting in death.

In 1887 Risdon Bennett, recently President of the Royal
College of Physicians, published a book, *The Diseases of the
Bible*,[3] which has still to be outdone by subsequent authors
for its sensible approach. He suggests that the quails had
eaten hellebore seeds, in which case veratrine, the active
principle of hellebore present in the quails, poisoned the
Israelites. Veratrine causes vomiting, diarrhoea, muscular
weakness (which may affect the muscles of the eye) and fall
in blood pressure. None of these symptoms is mentioned.
Death is unusual. It is more likely that the quails had eaten
seeds or other parts of monkshood (*Aconitum napellus*).

The active alkaloid is aconitine, which is very rapidly acting and dangerous even in small doses. It causes a burning sensation and tingling of the mouth, vomiting, fall in blood pressure and weak respiration, occasionally convulsions. Death ensues very quickly (sometimes drop-down) from cardiac and respiratory failure. Pharmaceutical preparations of aconitum are prepared from the root, but all parts of the plant are poisonous.

The quails were blown in from the sea (11:31). The Gulf of Suez is to the west of Taberah, but more likely the quails came from the north, that is the Mediterranean. In both directions, but particularly from the west, they would have had to cross a mountain range. Even though there is no record of aconitum growing in the Sinai Peninsula, death (11:33) while 'the meat was yet between their teeth' is strongly suggestive of aconitine poisoning. Tingling of the teeth is characteristic. Hellebore requires a rich soil, but aconitum is satisfied with a poor soil. For both veratrine and aconitine a remarkable species difference between quails and man must be postulated.

MIRIAM'S LEPROSY

Poor Miriam, a woman, copped it when she and her brother Aaron objected to Moses's marriage to a Cushite woman and criticised his position as a prophet with a special relationship with the Lord (12:2). The Cushite woman was Zipporah, daughter of Jethro (see page 99). In fact there was nothing remarkable about this: Miriam was criticising her sister-in-law as has been done many times before and since. Perhaps Miriam lacked tact. (Though Zipporah was described at her marriage as a Midianite, the Cushites and Kenites lived in the same region, north-east of the Gulf of Aqaba.) Nothing happened to Aaron, but Miriam (12:10) was punished by being made 'leprous, as white as snow' (see page 52).

Whatever Miriam was suffering from, it was not leprosy. 'As snow' suggests scaliness, which is not a characteristic of leprosy, and, more important, Miriam got better in seven days. Though Moses is described as 'very meek' there is no doubt that he was a formidable character, the more so when the anger of the Lord was kindled! Even so, the rapidity of Miriam's cure, seven days, suggests that she was suffering from a self-limiting condition. Every physician will know of patients with a vague illness for which no satisfactory explanation can be found until the skin starts to desquamate in fine flakes. The diagnosis is infection by a haemolytic *streptococcus* which, when of the throat, is called scarlet fever. Desquamation occurs some time between three days and three weeks after the start of the infection. The isolation for seven days outside the camp would stop Miriam from spreading infection. If Moses really did think she had leprosy, he did not observe the Levitical laws requiring purification, though these had not then been codified.

RECONNAISSANCE OF CANAAN

Shortly after Miriam recovered from scarlet fever, Moses was prompted to send out a reconnaissance party (which included Caleb and Hoshea, later renamed Joshua by Moses for no discernible reason) of twelve men, one from each tribe, to explore Canaan, the promised land (13:2). They reached Hebron and the Valley of Eshcol and all except Caleb concluded that although the land was 'flowing with milk and honey' (13:27) it was strongly fortified and the inhabitants (Amalekites, Hittites, Jebusites, Amorites, Canaanites and especially the Nephilim) were bigger than the Israelites, who thought of themselves as small. Caleb argued that the land should be occupied (13:30), but the rest of the party said that the land was poor, 'devours its inhabitants'. At this point the Israelites complained (14:2) that all Moses had done was to lead them to a barren wilderness. Would it not be better for their wives and little ones to return to Egypt?

Later, Caleb and Joshua had an attack of conscience and told the truth about the land (14:7), for which they were threatened with being stoned (14:10). After a lengthy conversation between Moses and the Lord (who condemned the adults but promised to preserve the children to be future shepherds) the ten men who had spoken evilly of the land died of plague (14:37). Caleb and Joshua survived. This gives a mortality rate of 83 per cent. The reconnaissance party was away for forty days (13:25) and may have been in close proximity with the current inhabitants: which would have allowed them to contract a specific fever such as measles, scarlet fever or smallpox. But this does not seem very likely. Smallpox is the only fever which would have caused such a high mortality and there is no mention of disease among the Israelites when they captured the land of Canaan.

The problem is to identify a disease which is contagious but not infective between man and man. Leptospirosis (Weil's disease or sewerman's disease) seems a likely candidate. A form of spirochaete, *Leptospira ictero-haemorrhagae,* is present in the urine and faeces of infected rats, and when these are excreted, water is very liable to be contaminated. On immersion (usually accidental) of the human skin, the spirochaete passes into the body tissues. The disease is very severe with a high mortality. Symptoms include small multiple haemorrhages under the skin and conjunctivae, jaundice and eventually liver and kidney failure.

Members of the expedition, other than Caleb and Joshua, may have been in contact with contaminated water, for example hiding behind the bank of a stream or pond. The incubation period is between three and forty days; the expedition was away forty days (13:25). The obvious objection to such a diagnosis is that there is no mention of jaundice, but this may not have been easily noticeable in a dark-skinned person.

REBELLION AGAINST MOSES

The clans of Korah, Dathan, Abiram and On started a rebellion against Moses (16:1). The account is confused and may cover two separate revolts. The cause seems to be partly restriction of priestly rights to the sons of Aaron (particularly on the part of the men of Korah who had affiliation with the Levites) and partly dissatisfaction with Moses's conduct in leading them into the wilderness where there was not even a vineyard, instead of into 'a land flowing with milk and honey' (16:14). Moses became angry with much self-justification. He told the 250 men of Korah to take their censers and burn incense the next morning. When they did so, fire came forth from the Lord and consumed them. The Lord told Moses and Aaron, who was also burning incense, to separate themselves from the others (16:20) so that they were not affected. To assume that 250 active men who were able to run from a fire were burnt to death seems absurd and it is difficult not to conclude that something lethal was created when the incense was burnt. The incident recalls the murder of Nadab and Abihu (see page 42). Most suspicious is that Eleazar was instructed by Moses immediately after the fire to recover the censers and to hammer them into plates. In other words, to destroy the evidence.

The second incident involved the clans of Dathan and Abiram, whose men, women and children, standing outside their tents, were, after a few threats by Moses, killed when 'the ground under them split asunder' (16:31). A landslide or an earthquake are possibilities.

Next day, when the survivors complained to Moses about the deaths, a cloud descended and caused the deaths of 14,700 persons (the number may be an exaggeration).

Once again Moses and Aaron separated themselves (16:45). Eventually the deaths stopped when Aaron took his censer, put fire in it and stood between the living and the dead. Unless the tent of meeting was over a volcanic vent which suddenly gave off hydrogen sulphide or sulphur dioxide, mass gassing of this order cannot be explained. Perhaps an ordinary cloud blew up and knowing the formidable nature of Moses when angered, the meeting decamped. A striking omission, which itself suggests that the numbers of dead were exaggerated, is that no account is given of the disposal of the corpses. A heap of 14,700 bodies being left to rot beggars description. There is no record of the sky being black with vultures. One thing must be remembered. Moses, like all successful politicans, had the ability to make it seem that he controlled events over which in fact he had no control.

Though Risdon Bennett,[3] writing in the light of knowledge in 1887, suggested that cholera or plague caused the deaths, neither of these diseases or any other infectious disease would observe the sanitary cordon of Aaron and his censer standing between the dead and the living. Ingestion of poison such as fungi, especially *Amanita phalloides* (deathcap) or toxin *Clostridium botulium* (causing botulism), is a possibility. This supposes that 14,700 persons ate a common meal and did not know that it had been poisoned either accidentally or deliberately. Both deathcap poisoning and botulism would result in rapid death.

DEATH OF MIRIAM AND AARON

Miriam's death is noted in passing (20:1). No doubt Aaron was failing (20:24), but Moses, in causing Aaron to be stripped of his clothes and left to die (probably of hypothermia) at the reputed age of 123 years on Mount Hor (20:26), was not observing the second commandment dictated by the Lord to him. At least, Eleazar to whom the holiness of his father passed when he assumed Aaron's clothes (29:28), had the benefit of keeping Aaron's lice within the family.

THE FLYING FIERY SERPENTS

During the journey to Edom the people complained of the lack of water and wholesome food (21:5). Following this they were afflicted with fiery serpents which bit them and many died. The Hebrew phrase describing the serpents is *serāphîm neḥāshîm*. The adjective *serāphîm* could be derived from the verb *sāraph*, 'to burn', thus referring to the burning effect of the bite of a poisonous snake, but the same word is used of the seraphim described in Isaiah 6:1, majestic beings with six wings. Also, the people asked Moses 'that the Lord take away the serpents from us' (21:7). It has therefore been argued that the fiery serpents were some form of flying creature.

If this is so, there are several possibilities. First, *Anopheles* mosquitoes which buzz when flying and have an irritating bite, may carry malaria and thus cause death. The objection to this suggestion is that the larvae need clean running water for propagation. Secondly, botflies, whose bite is excruciatingly painful, usually confine their attention to cattle, sheep or horses but may bite man. The occasional deposition of larvae under the skin may cause a creeping eruption. Though annoying, it is not fatal. Botflies breed in excrement and do not need water (apart from the moisture in the excrement).

Thirdly, guinea worm (*Dracunculus medinensis* or *Filaria medinensis*) is an idea which impressed Risdon Bennett.[3] The larvae in water enters a small water flea, *Cyclops*, just visible to the naked eye, which is swallowed when drinking. The larvae migrate to the tissues, taking ten to twelve months for the female to reach the gravid state. The male worm dies after impregnating the female. Isherwood *et al.*[4] have made an important discovery by finding a calcified male *dracunculus* in an Egyptian male mummy dating from about 1500 BC, slightly earlier than the time of Moses. Except when a deviant worm chooses a bizarre site, it comes to lie under the skin. An ulcer is formed over the anterior end of the worm and through it eggs are discharged into water, perpetuating the cycle. For this reason the ulcer is usually on the leg, though very rarely eggs may be discharged into a joint causing severe inflammation. The head of the worm protrudes slightly from the ulcer and the traditional method of removing the worm is by very carefully winding it round a small stick, about the size for example of a wooden skewer. If the worm is broken during the attempted removal ova are released into the tissues and the consequent allergic reaction is intense and would certainly justify the epithet 'fiery'. Female worms grow to about 2–4 feet (0.6–1.2 m) long, but may occasionally reach 6 feet (1.8m). The worm is often visible under the skin and this would be very alarming (*see Figure 4 and Figure 5*).

Guinea worm are prevalent in North Africa, including the Nile valley, and are likely to affect man where water is scarce, so that it becomes necessary to drink from stagnant pools. Indeed, the people complained of the shortage of water. Filtering through cloth or boiling removes *Cyclops*. Moses cured the sufferers by making a model in bronze of a serpent on a pole for them to look at (21:9) and this may have been the origin of the caduceus. If this suggestion is true, it means that the Israelites lived in insanitary conditions and continued to do so for at least one year. This lapse of time makes it worth looking at other, if outside, possibilities.

Fourthly, some centipedes have a painful, though inconsequential, bite. Centipedes, though small, may have a fearsome appearance. Fifthly, some species of cockroach may fly, though they do not bite. They breed in detritus and

Figure 4 'Indians drawing out guinea worms from their
legs: and in the summer sleeping in washing troughs'
*GH Velschius (1674) Exercitationes de Vena Medinensis et
de Vermiculis capillaribus infantium. Augsburg.*

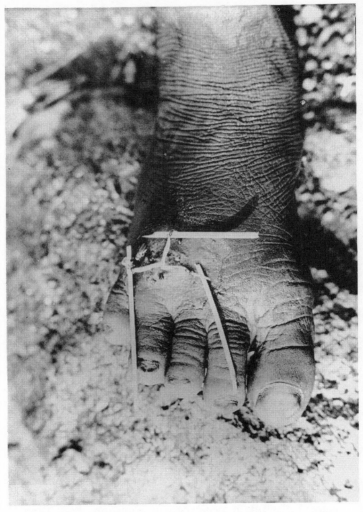

Figure 5 An unusual photograph from the Sudan, three
guinea worms emerging from one ulcer.

excrement and a separate water supply would not be needed. Death would not occur except from disease transmitted by organisms carried on their bodies.

Sixthly, infestation with body lice (*Pediculus humanus corporis* or *P. vestimenti*) seems a more likely suggestion than many others. Infestation with body lice, once known as the pearls of poverty, used to be thought a sign of sainthood. After his murder, the clothes of Thomas à Becket were found to be crawling with body lice. As soldiers found in the First World War when engaged in trench warfare (which necessitated living in close proximity), their bites can be intensely irritating. Eggs are deposited in the seams of clothing. Special centres for the steaming of soldiers' clothing had to be established. This was before the discovery of DDT. One of the medical wonders is the prevention of the spread of typhus transmitted by the body lice of refugees in Europe in the Second World War.

Body lice are 4–5 mm long and thus visible to the naked eye. When seen under magnification, they have a horrendous appearance. The life cycle is 2–3 weeks. The female lays about 300 eggs in ten days. Two other species of lice infect human beings: *P. capitis*,* (head lice which may be confused with dandruff), and *P. pubis*, the crab louse which infests the pubic hair and is nearly always spread venereally. Only the body louse (which in spite of its name lives in clothes, the other two species live on skin) carries disease. It has been shown to be the vector of epidemic typhus (*Rickettsia prowazekii*) and the less serious relapsing fever or trench fever (*Borrelia recurrentis*). The latter caused much disability in the First World War as a sufferer might be expected to be away from duty for eight weeks or more. Body lice have also been implicated in the spread of dog tapeworm. The circumstances of life among the early Israelites were

P. capitis have been discovered on an Egyptian mummy dating from about 3000 BC.

such that heavy infestation might be expected. When this happens the body is covered with myriads of bites. These may become infected, causing ulceration and subsequent scars. As a well-fed body louse excretes about 0.2 mg of faeces in 24 hours, this may be rubbed into the bites, resulting in punctate scars.

Though the Hebrew *neḥāshîm* is used elsewhere in the Bible to mean serpents or snakes (Genesis 3:13), including the bronze model of a serpent made by Moses (21:9), the feeling and appearance of body lice in the clothes or skin might well suggest serpents, even if they were small serpents. Formication (usually of psychological origin) is a feeling of ants under the skin. The conclusion that the fiery serpents were guinea worm (*Dracunculus medinensis*) is practically unavoidable.

MOABITE WOMEN AND MIDIANITES

While the Israelites were at Shittim they dallied with Moabite women (25:1) and afterwards ate a sacramental meal. Moses ordered the chiefs to be hanged, but this reparation to the Lord failed to stop an epidemic in which 24,000 persons died. Death seems to have occurred fairly quickly. To explain this, there is no need to introduce fanciful ideas[5] of a suddenly appearing infection by an AIDS-like virus not previously occurring and leaving no residuum. Food or waterborne disease, typhoid, cholera or shigella dysentery or any of the innumerable gastro-intestinal infections were almost certainly the cause. The murder of Zimri, an Israelite, and Cozbi, a Midianite woman (who were obviously not behaving as they should), by Phineas, Aaron's grandson and a priest, is reported to have stopped the epidemic (25:7–10).

Moses's response to the murder of Cozbi was curious. His wife, Zipporah, was a Midianite and her father had given him shelter and much useful advice (see page 99). Not only did he condone the murder but he ordered the Midianites to be harassed (25:16). The milk of human kindness was overwhelmed by the fear of backsliding by true believers. There are many cruel streaks in Moses's character but this unprovoked attack against the Midianites, even though it was described as a pre-emptive attack against Baal, shows him at his nastiest. All the males on the Midianite side were killed and Moses was angry that the Midianite women had been allowed to live (31:15). He ordered that all the captive women except the virgins should be murdered (31:17); the virgins should be kept for the Israelites. The returning warriors, if they had killed or touched a corpse, were ordered to purify themselves outside the camp (31:19). This would be normal ritual. Separate orders were issued that the warriors had to stay outside the camp for seven days. All this suggests that the Midianites, especially the women, were regarded as potential carriers of venereal disease, and the returning soldiers were regarded as potentially infected. Seven days isolation is grossly inadequate as gonorrhoea and other sexually transmitted disease may be latent for many years. If this was so, in the mores of the time, there would be no compunction in killing Cozbi and the other Midianite women. Moses and Eleazar did very well out of the booty, but it is not recorded whether they approved the general harlotry which must have resulted.

SECOND CENSUS

Before the attack on the Midianites, Moses and Eleazar again took a census of all men aged 20 or over (26:2). The male population of warring age amounted to 601,730 (26:51), slightly fewer than in the earlier census (1:2). The decline is not surprising in view of the butchery ordered by Moses, but he ascribed it to the deaths in the wilderness (26:65). There is no information about the number of women of childbearing age upon whom the size of the future population depended. These figures do not suggest a rapdily expanding population. Besides the expected mortality from infection, malnutrition and degenerative disease present in any population, the deaths of 38,960 persons are recorded as occurring in specific incidents in Numbers.

SACRIFICES

Rules for sacrificial offerings were also laid down (see page 56), but it is difficult to believe that 'a pleasing odour to the Lord' (29:2) arose from a burnt offering each year on the first day of the seventh month of one bull, one ram, seven male lambs, and one male goat together with cereal, oil and drink. The time and procedure for further festivals of sacrificial offering were also laid down. Starting on the fifteenth day of the seventh month and lasting for eight days, a total of 73 bulls, 112 lambs, 16 rams and 9 goats were offered. This was in addition to the regular burnt offerings, cereal offerings and drink offerings (29:12–40). More than a passing question must be the effect of all this on the food supply of people who complained not so long ago of starving in the wilderness.

INHERITANCE, DIVISION OF CANAAN, MANSLAUGHTER AND CITIES OF REFUGE

The second census disclosed that Zelophehad had no sons (27:1–4), and Moses, sitting with Eleazar, permitted his daughters to inherit and prescribed rules for future female inheritance. Daughters who inherited land might marry as they thought best, provided they married within the tribe of their father to prevent transfer of the land to another tribe (36:6).

Moses laid down the principles which should govern the division of the land of Canaan by Joshua and Eleazar among the tribes (34:1–29). The Levites, who had no share of the land, were to be given forty-eight cities, including six cities of refuge (35:6, 14). Three of the cities of refuge, Bezer, Ramoth and Golan were beyond the Jordan and the remaining three, Kedesh, Shechem and Hebron were in Canaan (Joshua 20:7). These six cities were probably chosen both because of their geographical situation and because they each possessed a famous sanctuary. Thus the institution of the cities of refuge is linked with the right of asylum recognised at the sanctuaries. Joab, who had murdered Abner and Amasa, was not protected by the law of asylum and was put to death in the sanctuary itself (see page 136). Moses sought to distinguish between accidental and deliberate killing. The man who was proved to have killed accidentally was safe in a city of refuge provided that he remained there until the death of the High Priest. Then he could return home. The man convicted of deliberate killing had to die because unavenged blood polluted the land and only the blood of the murderer could cleanse it.

References

1. Zuckerman S. *Social Life of Monkeys and Apes*. London: Kegan Paul, 1932.
2. Brim C.J. *Medicine in the Bible*. New York: Froben Press, 1936.
3. Risdon Bennett J. *The Diseases of the Bible*. London: Religious Tract Society, 1887.
4. Isherwood I., Jarvis H., Fawcett R.A. *Manchester Museum Mummy Project*, ed. David R.A. Manchester: Manchester University Press, 1979.
5. Gwilt J. Biblical Ills and Remedies. *Journal of the Royal Society of Medicine*. 1986, **79**: 738.

5

DEUTERONOMY
MOSES – THE MAN AND
THE PROPHET

STATURE OF ISRAELITES

King Og's bedstead (3:11) was·a minimum of 13½ feet (4.1 m) long and 6 feet (1.83 m) wide. If this reflects his stature rather than its use as a cushion for orgies, he was indeed a big man. Stature is determined in part genetically – and within a given race there will be the usual Gaussian distribution, so that at the extremes very small and very big men will be found – and in part by feeding, especially in early childhood. Og's height did not intimidate Moses: he was defeated by the Israelites (3:3).

There is no evidence that Semites who lived in Og's time (about 1200 BC) were big men. The Israelites thought of themselves as small (Numbers 13:33) compared with the Canaanites. It may well be that the hardships of agricultural and pastoral life during this era – 'In the sweat of your face you shall eat bread' (Genesis 3:19) – made it almost certain that food was scarce. Sacrifices to the Lord (Exodus 29:2, 11) would reduce, even if only marginally, the amount of food available for public consumption. If this is true, the small stature of the Israelites receives confirmation from very differing cultures. The doorways at Jarlshof used by the Picts are barely 4 feet (1.22 m) high. Og may be supposed to be a genetic sport at the end of the distribution curve. However, skeletons found at Gezer suggest that the height of Israelite men was about 5 feet 6 inches (1.67 m) and women 5 feet 3 inches (1.60 m),[1] which is a little less than the English today. Eliab, David's eldest brother (I Samuel 16:7) and Saul (I Samuel 9:2) were tall.

INTERMARRIAGE

In case intermarriage with the existing inhabitants of Canaan might deviate the Israelite partner from following the Lord, a tinge of racism raises its head (7:3).

SHECHITA AND HALAL

Deuteronomy 12:23 is the nastiest verse in the Bible, more explicit than Leviticus 17:11. 'Only be sure that you do not eat the blood.' The belief that life was in the blood doubtless derived from the beliefs of many primitive peoples. 'For the life of the flesh is in the blood; and I have given it for you upon the altar to make atonement for your souls; for it is the blood that makes atonement, by reason of the life' (Leviticus 17:11). The Israelites held that flesh might be eaten, but blood was assigned to the Lord and hence being sacred might not be eaten. This is spelled out specifically by verse 12:23. Noah was told not to eat flesh containing blood (Genesis 9:4). Cain was cursed by the ground on which Abel's blood had been spilt (Genesis 4:10).

The freedom of all men to hold whatever religious beliefs they wish is absolute. It is the rituals which surround those beliefs which must be questioned. If the Jews and Muslims do not want to eat pork, that is a private affair of no great importance except to themselves. But to condemn animals to being hung upside down suffering death by exsanguination after their necks are cut is a matter of public concern. In Britain, animals are stunned first, but this practice is not followed in many – possibly most – countries. Electrical recording shows that brain activity may continue for 126 seconds after throat slitting but is lost instantaneously after stunning with a gun. Jewish (Shechita) and Muslim (Halal) require the animal to be whole, but Muslims are prepared to accept meat stunned before slaughter. Livestock breeders should question their consciences before exporting cattle and sheep. To expect cruelty to disappear throughout the world is, alas, too much to hope, but acts of cruelty by individuals are different from systemising it in rituals, especially religious rituals.

Quite properly, in September 1989, when beagle puppies which were being exported from Britain to a pharmaceutical company in Sweden to be used for animal experiments were suffocated while on the ship *Tor Britannia*, there was public horror. The export of sheep to Middle East countries from Europe, Australia and New Zealand evokes no response. The two minutes which the sheep take to die with their throats cut must seem a very long while.

LEGITIMACY

Again the pouring of blood on the altar and burning of flesh which may be eaten are emphasised (12:27). Even for close relatives or one's wife who may have worshipped other gods, no mercy was permitted for deviation from the Mosaic covenant (13:10, 17:5). Stoning to death was obligatory (see page 218). Incidentally the victim of stoning and of hanging was unclean as the body still contained blood. A man falsely accusing his bride of not being a virgin was whipped and fined (22:18). If, in fact, she was not a virgin at marriage, she was stoned to death in front of her father's house (22:21). All this from the mouth of Moses, who earlier had promulgated the Ten Commandments (5:6–21) and who was otherwise proclaiming most admirable precepts.

In a society so devoted to the propagation of the male gene, captive women (21:10ff.) and slave-girls had to be protected against sexual aggression, probably because of the lack of choice on their part; the rape of a betrothed virgin (22:24) results in one or both parties being stoned to death. If the offence occurs in the city and the woman does not cry for help, both die, but if the offence occurs in the countryside, where there is no one to rescue the woman, only the man dies. If a wife trying to rescue her husband in a fight, grasps the opponent's genitals, that hand shall be cut off (25:12). A newly married man is excused military service for one year (24:5), doubtless to ensure procreation. In point of fact, signs of loss of virginity in a woman are often minimal; not only may the hymen be rudimentary, but the first intercourse usually occurs, contrary to much folklore, without pain or bleeding. Male violence is of major importance.

Clearly in such a society, transvestites and homosexuals would be disliked (22:5). Rarely, tranvestism occurs in assocation with homosexuality; it is most often to be regarded as an abnormality (commoner in men than in women) bordering on a delusion. Sexual satisfaction is not derived from dressing up. Though many transvestites marry and some have children, society dislikes abnormalities especially when they are thought of as hindering procreation. Whatever Joan of Arc's true offence may have been, dressing in male clothes was raised as the justification for burning her at the stake.[2]

CRUSHED TESTICLES

Chapters 21, 22, 23 and also 27 contain good moral precepts, some designed to prevent consanguinity which would be genetically harmful. Crushed testicles (23:1), Hebrew *merôah*, means a rubbing away or enlargement of the testicles. Virtually any disease of the testes and epididymus would come within such a wide definition. Rubbing away might include atrophy of the testes after mumps, an undescended testicle or (rarely) castration. Enlargement might be due to a tumour, bacterial epididymitis (most likely to be gonorrhoeal), or tuberculous epididymo-orchitis. A hydrocele or variocele would mimic enlargement of the testis. Mutilation or loss of the penis is envisaged. The commonest cause would be ablation by a careless circumcision or mutilation, either as a punishment or self-inflicted by a lunatic, but rarely cancer (see page 17).

SAFETY, HYGIENE AND STARVATION

A safety parapet had to be installed around the roofs of new houses (22:8).

A place outside the camp had to be appointed (and used) as a latrine (23:12) and a special digging stick carried with weapons to bury excreta (23:13) – which makes it the more important not to get hold of the wrong end of the stick!

The reference (28:56) to cannibalism during a siege does not say anything about kosher. The 'most tender and delicately bred woman' (28:56) will not share with her husband, son or daughter her placenta or any boy or girl she may bear. She will eat them herself. It is nice to know that Moses recognised that there were such women!

EXTRAORDINARY AFFLICTIONS

The concluding chapters of Deuteronomy are a mixture of blessings falling on those who observe the law and penalties to be heaped on those who do not. Once more Moses threatens (28:59) that the Lord will heap 'extraordinary afflictions, afflictions severe and lasting and sickness grievous and lasting' together with 'all the diseases of Egypt' on disobedient Israelites and their offspring. In addition to diseases the list of curses includes blindness, exposure of the slain, sexual violation of the offender's wife, pillage, destruction of crops and the enslavement of children. Weinfeld[3] has pointed out that this list is almost identical with the list of curses prescribed in the Vassal-Treaties of Esarhaddon, King of Assyria (690 – 669 BC),[4] as punishments for breaking the treaties. Apart from these two instances no other series of maledictions has been found in ancient Near Eastern literature and Weinfeld suggests that a Jewish scribe copied the curses from the Assyrian treaty document and made them appropriate to those who disobeyed the Lord's commands.

To get a glimmer of what the 'diseases of Egypt' might have been and their devastating consequences one has only to look at the chapter on infectious disease in the first edition of *Osler's Principles and Practice of Medicine* published in 1892. In describing disease more or less specific to the Middle East, it is easy to forget that Egypt and Palestine were, by present Western standards, grossly insanitary. Dust spread faeces, water and milk were contaminated to a degree that beggars description, overcrowding in unventilated tents and huts was the rule. However much the Israelites were enjoined to wash (Jeremiah 2:22) they did this with lye (a caustic solution made by dissolving wood ash in water). Wood for cooking and heating was hard to come by. Typhoid and salmonella infections, cholera (28:22), infectious hepatitis, tuberculosis including pulmonary, abdominal and bone, smallpox, measles, whooping cough, diptheria and tetanus would be either endemic or epidemic from time to time. Staphylococcal (28:27) and fungal (28:22) infections of the skin would be commonplace.

Of particular importance would be streptococcal infections. Not only would *streptococcus* directly cause morbidity and mortality from quinsy, erysipelas (28:22), sepsis in wounds and puerperal sepsis, but immune response to the antigen (of the Group A haemolytic type of *streptococcus*) is the cause of rheumatic fever which so often has as its sequelae heart disease. The heart muscles are weakened (reducing the amount of effort that can be exerted), all the valves of the heart may be affected, the most common being the mitral valve. Rachel (see page 13) almost certainly suffered from rheumatic myocarditis and mitral stenosis. The truly devastating effects of rheumatic disease (to be distinguished from 'rheumatism', a confusion which has doubtless arisen from the muscular pains in the acute phase of rheumatic fever) are only too familiar to those who practised medicine in Britain early this century or who practise in developing countries today. Treatment of streptococcal infections, including those causing sore throat, with penicillin (or other antibiotic) has virtually eliminated rheumatic fever (and all its consequences) in Western countries.

SEXUALLY TRANSMITTED DISEASES

The Israelites (or rather Moses) deplored the sexual and other orgies associated with the worship of Baal (Numbers 25:5), even to the point of punishment by hanging. Even so, the most cursory reading of Leviticus and Numbers leaves an impression that gonorrhoea was common (see pages 65 and 87).

Ulceration of the cornea in the new born whose eyes are contaminated by *Neisseria gonorrhoae* during birth is an important cause of blindness. So, too, is infection in a similar manner by *chlamydia trachomatis*, possibly best classified as a large virus rather than a bacteria, which causes neo-natal *chlamydia ophthalmia*. Very occasionally, *chlamydia* may be transmitted non-venereally, for example in swimming-baths. In Britain, about 3 per cent of women suffer from vaginal or cervical *chlamydia* infection (which is usually symptomless, but which none the less is an important cause of salpingitis, and hence sterility) but fewer than 1 per cent of babies born have their eyes infected. Trachoma may result and be followed by scarring of the cornea, but fortunately effective treatment is now available. *Chlamydia* infection of the genital tract must be regarded as a venereal disease being transmitted by males. Most trachoma affecting some 500 million people (of whom some 5 to 10 million are blind) is also caused by *chlamydia* infection, which is directly transmitted from eye to eye by flies in children living in overcrowded and squalid conditions in developing countries. Early treatment will prevent scarring and if this has occurred, surgery may help to alleviate blindness.

Other sexually transmitted diseases include *trichoniasis vaginalis* caused by a small protozoan. Though vaginal irritation is intense it is easily cured. Mostly in tropical countries, *granuloma inguinale* (caused by an organism related to *chlamydia*) causes ulceration of the genitals and the surrounding tissues. Before the Second World War soft chancre (*Haemophilus ducreyi*) caused some worry as a possible differential diagnosis of hard chancre which occurs in syphilis. Soft chancre can easily be cured with sulphonamides. Genital herpes is distressing and even painful. Caused by the Human Papilloma Virus, spread by the male to an uninfected female, HPV is causally incriminated with carcinoma of the cervix (see page 17). It is tempting to suppose that the blindness and madness (28:28) were due to syphilis in the tertiary stage. Syphilis was not present outside the New World until Christopher Columbus's sailors brought it back. It was first noticed when they were engaged in besieging Naples in AD 1495 (see page 69).

BIRDS

The Royal Society for the Protection of Birds would give qualified approval to 22:6 as it requires the nesting bird to be left alone, though any young birds may be taken.

MOSES – THE MAN AND THE PROPHET

he first five books of the Old Testament, the Pentateuch, are ascribed to Moses. The first book, Genesis, is certainly nothing to do with him, and it must be conjecture how much the actions of one man contributed to the traditions underlying the other four books. Moses dominated and moulded the early Hebrew nation, and so consideration of his personality is not out of place.

Amram of the tribe of Levi married his father's sister, Jochebed, and their children were Miriam, Aaron and Moses. Moses's mother may have had particular reasons for exposing her child to the hazards of floating in a capsule in the reeds along the Nile besides obedience to Pharaoh's command. The maid conveniently at hand when Pharaoh's daughter found Moses was probably Miriam.[5] This strengthens the impression of a put-up job. Whoever was on the bank was able to arrange for Moses to be returned to his natural mother for nursing and she was paid to bring up her own child (Exodus 2:9).

Brim[6] gives credence to a Rabbinical exegesis that Moses was a premature child born at twenty-eight weeks. If so, his survival is a notable credit to his mother: further, his mother disposed of him only when Pharaoh's spies knew she should have reached term. An accepted method of disposing of unwanted or weakly children (Moses's mother waited to find he was goodly before acting) since Babylonian times was to deposit them in the river in a closed water-proof capsule. This part of Moses's story is not unique. For one thing, the story of King Sargon, who reigned over Babylonia in 2600 BC is similar. The Indian epic *Mahabharatra* contains analogous tales and a similar tradition occurs in Japanese stories. Whatever reason Pharaoh's daughter gave for choosing the name Moses, it has the same root as Ra-moses, the god-king. Pharaohs were god-kings.

JETHRO

After being brought up at the Egyptian court, Moses murdered an Egyptian (Exodus 2:12). He was angry at seeing a Hebrew beaten but with surprising circumspection Moses looked around before killing the Egyptian. He thought he had not been noticed, but the next day, when he intervened in a fight between two Hebrews, one of them referred to the killing and asked who had made Moses a prince and a judge (Exodus 2:14). This incident is a foretaste of Moses's later characteristics, quick indignation and action coupled with lordly behaviour and circumspection.

Prudently, Moses fled to Midian, where he prevented shepherds interfering when the seven daughters of Jethro, a Midianite priest, were watering their father's sheep. As a result of so doing he found board and lodging and a wife, Zipporah, who was one of Jethro's daughters (Exodus 2:21). Marriage to an Israelite was not opposed (indeed may have been welcomed, considering the exacting life facing an unmarried woman in Semitic society). With the death of Pharaoh, Moses judged it safe to return to Egypt.

Jethro seems to have been a kind man and a wise confidant. When Moses was encamped near Mount Sinai during the journey to Canaan, Jethro visited him and saw that Moses was overburdened with the task of judging disputes among the people. He advised him to delegate some of his work by appointing able men to administer justice, reserving to himself only the most difficult cases (Exodus 18:18). Moses accepted the advice of his father-in-law.

CONFLICT

The life of a shepherd was uneventful, not to say dull, but, however exciting the life of an Egyptian prince, his murder of an Egyptian committed Moses to the Israelite cause. Conflict of desires existed. Moses suffered from a dissociated state at a high level of consciousness and underwent a non-specific reaction.[7] As always, the result was a compelling certainty which conveniently could be couched in terms of messages from God. Moses was able to rise above personal terms and speak from the heart of men yearning for freedom. Moses led the Israelites to Canaan and like the Pharaohs founded a dynasty which, unlike that of the Pharaohs, continues to this day. If Moses was suffering from neurosis, so too were other great men. If he had defects — and he did, ruthlessness and vanity — this was the price to be paid, as all artists have to pay in some form, for his creativity.

Moses seems to have been able to mix religion and politics. 'Your murmurings are not against us but against the Lord' (Exodus 16:8). There is no particular reason to suppose that the plagues which vexed Pharaoh were special or isolated events. More probably Moses had the wit to invoke natural occurrences as the Lord's punishment.

Looked at from the Egyptian point of view, the defection of small family or tribal groups of Israelites was an annoying disturbance in industrial relations. True, some labour was lost, but this was not important and was counterbalanced by the removal of the prime agitator. 'How long shall this man be a snare to us? Let the men go ... do you not yet understand that Egypt is ruined?' (Exodus 10:7). Indeed, it may be wondered whether the Egyptian pursuit was any more than seeing the Israelites on their way with no serious intention of capture. Moses was no more than a renegade minor official.[8] In the end, the Egyptians could not let them go quickly enough (Exodus 12:33).

MOSES-PHARAOH

'And they [the Israelites] believed in the Lord and in his servant Moses' (Exodus 14:31). The song of Miriam, Moses's sister (Exodus 15:21), cannot but have endowed Moses with reflected glory from the Lord. It was Moses who was seen to stretch out his hand over the sea (Exodus 14:26).

The story of the tablets suggests that Moses, when at the top of Mount Sinai, confused his memory-images with the god-Pharaoh and, when at the bottom, with the law-giving of the king-Pharaoh. When the Israelites entered the desert, it was inhabited, even if sparsely, by other peoples. Mount Sinai (or Mount Horeb) is known to have been the haunt of holy men[9] (possibly living in small communes scattered throughout the Levant) and it is more than likely that Moses took advice from them. If the tablets really were of stone, carving them would be the work of several men; if of clay, the writing would be heroic work for one man. This is not to say that the Ten Commandments (Exodus 20:1ff.), even if partially derived from the Babylonians, are not a good guide to human conduct. The Covenant gave Moses a means of controlling a 'stiff-necked' people (Exodus 33:5). The elaborations (Exodus 21:20–35, 22, 26) following the Ten Commandments, whether read as law or guidelines, are humane. Women derived very considerable protection and even the status of slave girls was enhanced.

Mental activity not arising from immediate perceptions arises from memory-images. Recall of past experiences does not result in unaltered and more or less isolated recollections but in the active organisation of past experiences. Besides Pharaoh-like memories, Moses seems to have had a full even to excess measure of collective psychic life. The resultant drive raised Moses above his personal psychic life (of the Pharaoh-like complex) to accredit Yahweh (Exodus 3:14) to the tribes in Egypt,[10] so that Yahweh became the fount of the personal and social life of the Israelites. In a harsh and ruthless period of history Moses's excesses, e.g. his apparent callousness (or connivance) at the death of Aaron's sons (Leviticus 10:1), Aaron's lonely death (Numbers 33:38), organised fratricide (Exodus 32:27) – every man was to kill his brother, but Moses did not attempt to kill Aaron – and the murder of Korah and his company (Numbers 16:31), may not have been so bad as they seem to us. Cruel or not, they were subordinate to Moses's total commitment to the tribes whom he saw as his people. They might even excuse Moses's manipulation of the wrath of the Lord to control an unruly mob. Moses fulfilled the requirements of a great leader. He was able to make events over which he had no control look as if they had been organised by him.

VOICE OF GOD

Moses was an expatriate, more Hebrew than the Hebrews, rejecting his Egyptian upbringing and hankering after his lost culture. Suffering from a sense of injustice at the hands of the Egyptians, he had a mind finely attuned to the ethos of a nation which owed its very existence to Abraham's obedience to the voice of God. Never mind what the voice of God was: that was the tradition of his tribe and of his times. Trying to express the traditions of his nation, his mind was conditioned to interpret his longings as the voice of God. To do so made them irresistibly authoritative.

Overload of the mental mechanism results in emotional collapse. The Bible abounds in examples when unbearable stimuli are avoided by sublimation or suppression (the most notable being Zechariah's dumbness (see page 201), and Saul's blindness on the road to Damascus (see page 243)). The mind is dissociated. Persons vary widely in the ease with which this happens; culture and previous 'practice' are important influences. For Moses frustrated ambition was the stimulus when a thorn bush appeared to be on fire without being burnt (Exodus 3:2). The most likely explanation was that the shimmering heat waves above the bush were responsible for the physical appearance which was given significance in Moses's suggestible state.

Throughout the Old Testament, prophets had a sense of mission, spending much time (often in isolation) meditating on supposed or real deviations from the will of God. Fasting, isolation, prayer and self-flagellation weakens resistance to dissociation. Only a mild degree of dissociation is needed for thoughts normally unacceptable to have an unjustified significance (i.e. originating from God). Some religious movements or cults use the susceptibility following emotional release (hell-fire preaching or orgasm) as a means of conversion. Dissociation is a protective mechanism, and therefore normal, but it can lead to neuroses requiring urgent therapy. Whether the resulting prophecy is called a daydream, mental perception, hysterical fugue, numinous state, witchcraft or voodoo is not important. It is not a delusion which implies loss of sanity.

Moses's self-questionings were interpreted as the voice of God, and who, in the prevailing culture, was to say that Moses's strong, almost ineffable sense of destiny of the people of Israel was otherwise? It is remarkable how often the voice of God coincided with the desires of the people. Moses was educated and intelligent. One danger is that lesser men will use the voice of God to explain and justify what they do not understand and thus be led to reprehensible action. Unlike the voices heard by schizophrenic or paranoid personalities, Moses's voices were firmly in contact with reality – the reality of his past experiences and present circumstances. The danger of voices, including the voice of God, is that they are pathological, arising from disordered brain processes, for example paranoid persons will be told to (and do) kill. Even self-hypnosis and self-deception may generate dangerous convictions. To say the least, voices, no matter from whom they are supposed to come, are very dangerous. Even Moses towards the end of his life showed paranoid ruthlessness. Men like to have explanations of (or a scapegoat for) their affairs; within the knowledge of the time, attribution of what they did not understand to the Lord (by voices or otherwise) was as good an explanation as any other. Even Solomon explained his dreams as the appearance of the Lord (I Kings 3:10). Perhaps, for Moses, the voice of the Lord was no more than a means of getting an unruly congregation to do what was sensible.

DEATH OF MOSES

Moses, when he died at the reputed age of 120 years, must have been a very fit old man as immediately before his death he climbed Mount Nebo (34:1), which is 3760 feet (1146 m) high. Like so many mortals he did not survive to see the full fruits of his life's work. Though his death as recorded was foreordained by the Lord, after such a feat in old age ischaemic heart disease is a likely cause (34:7). At least, he did not have Parkinson's disease or senile degeneration of the brain.

References

1. Wolff H.W. *Anthropology of the Old Testament*. London: SCM Press, 1974.
2. Ratnasuriya R.H. Joan of Arc, creative psychopath: is there another explanation? *Journal of the Royal Society of Medicine*. 1986, 79: 234.
3. Weinfeld M. *Deuteronomy and the Deuteronomic School*. Oxford: Clarendon Press, 1972.
4. Pritchard J.B. *Ancient Near Eastern Texts relating to the Old Testament*. Princeton: Princeton University Press, 1969.
5. Buber M. *Moses*. London: East and West Press, 1946.
6. Brim C.J. *Medicine in the Bible*. New York: Froben Press, 1936.
7. Sargant W. *The Mind Possessed*. London: Heinemann, 1973.
8. Posner E.J. *Dictionary of Egyptian Civilisation*. London: Methuen, 1962.
9. Field M.J. *Angels and Ministers of Grace*. London: Longman, 1971.
10. Blunt A.W.F. *Israel Before Christ*. London: Oxford University Press, 1924.

6

JOSHUA

Joshua was appointed by Moses to succeed him as leader of the people of Israel (Numbers 27:18), with Eleazar, who succeeded his father Aaron as High Priest (Numbers 20:26), playing an important part as coadjutor.

CIRCUMCISION

The most charitable thing that can be said about the book of Joshua is that it is unsuitable for children. Small girls who did not know what circumcision was would certainly do so before the end of Chapter 5. The Jews were far from alone in symbolising their religious and national identity in mutilation of the penis, but they may have been alone in believing that circumcision was a sign of the covenant with their God (see page 16). Today circumcision is compulsory for Muslims, frequent among Hindus and a widespread practice among the tribes of Borneo, New Guinea and most tribes of Africa. Until very recent times some tribes used to decorate the penis by piercing the frenum and wearing sticks of wood, bones and even the cotter pins of outboard motors. The mass orgies of mutilation recorded in 5:8 would give rise to much haemorrhage and sepsis. No wonder they 'remained in their places . . . till they were healed'. Besides the physical trauma, circumcision is frightening and fraught with psychological sequelae.

Before he attacked Jericho, Joshua circumcised those men born during the Exodus (surprisingly this did not extinguish their desire to fight) thus sanctifying the army and ensuring that Yahweh was on their side. Gideon (see page 112) also made great play of doing this. Deborah (Judges 5:15) expressed surprise at the willingness of men to fight. The word Israel means 'El (god) does battle'. Few wars, even those of recent times, have been fought without God on the side of the army, even if this means that he is on both sides.

RAHAB

The wages of sin lay not so much in death as in treachery. Rahab, a prostitute, who had hidden the two men sent by Joshua to spy out the land, thus saved her own life and those of her father's household (6:22). Perhaps this had more to do with the fall of Jericho than the trumpets and shouting. Rahab continued to live in Israel.

JOSHUA'S MURDERS AND MASSACRES

Achan's disobedience in stealing a beautiful mantle, 200 shekels of silver and a bar of gold (7:21), all of which were sacred to the Lord, resulted in the vicious murder of him and all his family and animals by stoning (7:27).

At one point before the fall of Jericho, Joshua was reassured by an angel of the Lord (5:13) that he was right to continue the conquest of Canaan. Up to then the slaughter (and there had been plenty of it) had been more or less casual, but the systematic slaughter started with the killing of all the inhabitants of Ai (8:22). The king was captured and killed later (8:29), thus completing the elimination. The claim is made (11:22) that only in Gaza, Gath and Ashdod were a few persons left alive. In all, thirteen tribes were, according to the account, exterminated.

The conquered land was shared among the tribes of Israel (14:13, 15:1), thus securing a respite from war. Once more the distinction between manslaughter and murder is made, this time by Joshua (a curious act by one who instigated genocide) in designating Kedesh, Shechem and Hebron as cities of refuge (20:7) (see page 88).

DEATH OF JOSHUA

Joshua is reputed to have died aged 110 years, which for the safety of life and limb in Canaan was much too late. His bones were buried at Shechem (24:32).

7

JUDGES

Most of the book of Judges is concerned with events during the conquest of Canaan by the Israelites, which, according to the author, fell into a neat pattern. Disobedience to the commandments of the Lord meant hardship and defeat, while obedience, under a judge (ruler) whom the Lord had selected, meant deliverance and victory.

TOES AND THUMBS

Adonibezek's loss of his great toes (1:6) would not be a serious disability, probably confined to difficulty in jumping or springing. The loss of his thumbs would be very serious – opposition of the thumbs to the fingers cannot occur so that articles cannot be picked up, except by using fingers as claws against the palm. The human ability to oppose fingers and thumb is an important difference between man and monkeys. Most apes have the ability to oppose finger and thumb, thus facilitating the use of tools. Indeed, apes may use different tools (each adapted to its purpose) sequentially to achieve a designated objective (see Figure 6).

MARRIAGE

Poor Achsah (1:12) was given by Caleb to be the wife of Othniel as a reward for conquering Debir, but she was clever enough to obtain a present of some springs from Caleb. Perhaps this softened the insult of unloving intercourse. Caleb also distinguished himself by having intercourse with Ephrathah, his father's widow, who as a result bore him a son. As recorded (I Chronicles 2:21–26), the family indulged in sex for all.

The effect on the individual persona of such proceedings depends on cultural expectations. Among primitive peoples the subsequent wives are welcomed without jealousy and in the U.S.A. children accept serial marriages without much disturbance.

OBESITY AND MURDER

Ehud girded his sword on his right thigh because he was left-handed (3:16). Eglon, subsequently murdered by Ehud (3:21), was a very fat man and had a cool chamber. He seems to have used this cool chamber as a privy and it was while at his privy that he was murdered (3:25). African tribes construct chambers for their chief out of straw. Such chambers have double roofs and walls, each layer separated by about 2 feet (0.6 m) with circulating air between. If the outside roof is of aluminium sheet (not corrugated iron) the sun is reflected and the cooling effect greater.

Genetic diseases causing obesity are rare, and when they do occur may be associated with other abnormalities such as hypogonadism, short stature, polydactylism or retarded mental processes. Obesity is often associated with diseases such as hypothyroidism, Cushing's syndrome or the administration of drugs such as contraceptive pills. 'Simple' obesity tends to run in families. Fat parents (particularly fat mothers) tend to have fat children. The evidence that this may have an inherited basis is not strong, but the example of overeating is important. The major cause of obesity is excessive food intake. Exercise plays only a small part (if any) in the correction of obesity. To burn up 1 lb (0.45 kg) of body

Figure 6. Ape opposing thumb and using tool.

fat one has to walk 66½ miles (111 km) at 3½ miles (5.33 km) per hour. Such part as exercise does play is to increase the lean body mass in relation to fat. However caused, obesity carries with it increased and earlier mortality.

Under Ehud, who, all said and done, was a murderer and a nasty one at that, Israel conquered the Moabites, to whom they had been enslaved for eighteen years (3:14), and killed 10,000 able-bodied men (3:29). Seemingly, the intention was to reduce or eliminate the size of potential enemy armies. Shamgar killed a further 600 Philistines (3:31).

DEBORAH

Once more the people of Israel were enslaved, this time to Jabin, who reigned in Hazor (4:2). Deborah, a prophetess who at that time judged Israel, commanded Barak to organise an army of 10,000 to raze Hazor. Sensibly, Barak refused to go unless Deborah came with him (4:8). Jabin's army was defeated and its general Sisera fled and sought refuge with Jael, wife of Heber, who was encamped nearby. Jael persuaded Sisera to interrupt his flight, promising that he would be safe in her husband's tent. After wrapping Sisera in a rug, Jael, using a hammer, drove a tent peg* into his temple (4:21). Deborah's governance imposed order on anarchy, and she must have been an outstanding woman to earn the loyalty of the local warlords. Apparently murder and killing was acceptable, as was brutal deceit (4:21), but acceptance of alien gods was not. Deborah, with Barak, praised deceit in song (5:24) and lauded the distribution of a 'maiden or two for every man' as spoil (5:30). Barak may have contributed this thought, but Deborah remained feminine enough to suggest two embroidered scarves for the mother of Sisera.

---

*The Hebrew for tent peg yāthēdh is also used for digging stick (see page 94)

GIDEON'S CHILDREN

When Gideon chose 300 men to fight the Midianites and the Amalekites by selecting those who lapped water from the Jordan like a dog (7:5), it is tempting to read some public health significance into this. Any infection that might be transferred from the mouths of even 300 men to the water would be insignificant. Before the battle, Gideon was reassured by the interpretation of a dream which promised him victory. After surrounding the Midianite camp and engendering fear by blowing trumpets, the Israelite army routed the Midianites.

Gideon having begat seventy sons from many wives (8:30) – and at least one by his concubine – any girls (who on the normal sex ratio would number sixty-three) interspersed between the boys are not worthy of mention; Gideon died of exhaustion having fathered 133 children.

Another judge who was prolific was Ibzan (12:8) but he had only thirty sons and thirty daughters. Both sons and daughters were given in marriage outside the clan, their prospective wives and husbands carefully chosen no doubt to avoid pollution of the Israelite religion. Abdon had forty sons (12:14), again, daughters are not worth mentioning.

HUMAN SACRIFICE

During another tribal war against the Ammonites, Jephthah, who was now judge of the Israelites (11:30), made a vow that if he won the battle the first person greeting him on his return to his house would be sacrificed to the Lord. As might be expected, his daughter and only child ran out of the door to greet him and because of Jephthah's vow agreed to be sacrificed. The daughter's age, though not stated, may be inferred as being pubescent or early adolescent, not less than 16 years old. All that she asked for was to be given two months' grace to wander the mountains with her friends (during which time she promised to remain a virgin, presumably so that her sacrifice might be the more beneficial) before returning to be slaughtered by her father.

SPIES

Pronunciation is cultural, like the Israelites' use of the word 'Shibboleth' to detect fugitives from Ephraim (12:6); the Dutch in the Second World War required suspected German spies to enunciate 'Schleveningen', the name of a seaside town near The Hague.

BIRTH OF SAMSON

In the story of the infertile couple Manoah and his wife (again 'the woman') who desired a child (13:2), an angel of the Lord (see page 15) as becomes apparent almost certainly a man, appeared before the woman and told her she would bear a son. He went on to advise her to avoid alcohol. After prayers by Manoah and his wife that the angel would come again, he made a second appearance to the woman as she sat in a field. This time it is specifically said that her husband was not present. The woman ran to tell her husband, who arose and went to the angel. A lengthy conversation ensued culminating in Manoah offering sacrifice in the presence of the angel. It is very difficult to avoid the conclusion that the angel of the Lord fathered the resulting conception and that the cause of the infertility lay in Manoah. In due course Samson was born.

SAMSON

Samson was unfortunate in his choice of women (14:1; 16:1, 4). Almost certainly spoilt as a child, he was unable to inspire loyalty in them. Perhaps they were no more than fickle. The unnamed Philistine woman who lived at

Timnah (14:1) and whom he married, betrayed him to her countrymen under the threat of the destruction of her father's house. Not surprisingly Samson left her and she was 'given' to his best man (14:20). When Samson (15:1) was refused access to his ex-wife, he rejected her sister (whom the father was prepared to give to him) as a substitute. He pretended he was blameless when he did mischief to the Philistines by letting foxes shackled in pairs, with blazing torches tied to their tails (15:4) loose among their corn. He was bound by the men of Judah (15:13) and was handed over to the Philistines but broke fetters of new rope before killing more Philistines, this time with the jawbone of an ass. With the harlot in Gaza (16:1) Samson got what he might have expected. The men of the town decided to kill him, but before they could act Samson pulled up the gate of the city with the posts and carried them away. Samson's fate after Delilah had betrayed him to the Philistines for money was very cruel indeed. He had his eyes gouged out (16:21).

His behaviour suggests mental impairment and this may, implausibly, be related to an X-linked muscular dystrophy (Thomsen's disease). A number of overlapping clinical syndromes have been described. One of these is myotonic congenita in which the onset of the loss of muscle strength may be delayed for between twenty and fifty years. Loss of muscle strength is associated with slow muscle relaxation which may falsely give the impression of strength. Because Samson was a Nazarite, he did not cut his hair. He prevaricated in his answers to Delilah's importunate questioning about the source of his strength but eventually told her that it lay in his hair. Delilah sent for a man to shave Samson's head while he lay asleep in her lap (16:19). Fortuitously, this coincided with the onset of the symptoms. Some of the myotonic syndromes are associated with blindness. Even though the house of Dagon at Gaza which the blind Samson pushed down was built by the Phoenicians and therefore might be supposed to be strong, it does seem to have been overcrowded (3000 men and women on the roof alone in addition to the lords and others in the house) and relatively little effort by Samson could have caused it to collapse (16:27ff.). Maybe, Samson was a psychopath wanting more love than he was able to give, continuing the behaviour of a spoilt and much wanted child throughout life.

GANG RAPE OF CONCUBINE

Chapters 19 and 20 are the equivalent of video nasties. After ill-treating his concubine, causing her to leave him, an unnamed Levite fetched her from her father's house. On the way home he gave her to the Benjaminites, loutish youths of Gibeah, to be ravished and abused to save him from having to submit to homosexual intercourse with the youths (19:25).[1] In the morning she was dead. He took her home and cut her into twelve pieces (19:29), which in fact would be a very difficult and very messy operation. The Levite's punishment was no more than being ostracised, but clearly there was much justified indignation. A tribal gathering agreed that an army consisting of one-tenth of the men of each tribe, in total numbering 400,000, should attack the Benjaminites in Gibeah, ostensibly for revenge. The Benjaminites, for their part, numbered 26,700 men. Among these latter were 700 picked men who were left-handed: every one of whom could sling a stone at a hair and not miss (20:16). In an unselected population of the same size the number of left-handers would be about 1200. After suffering 40,000 dead (clearly an exaggeration) the Israelites enticed the Benjaminites into leaving Gibeah and defeated them.

ALCOHOL

Afterwards there was trouble in finding sufficient Israelite women to become wives for the Benjaminite men remaining after the slaughter (21:16) because the other tribes had sworn they would not give their daughters in marriage to men of the tribe of Benjamin. There were not many Benjaminites left as 25,000(!) had been slain (20:46). They were first given 400 virgins from Jabesh-gilead, but that was not enough (21:14). Then the Benjaminites were advised to steal wives from the dancers at a festival at Shiloh (21:20). Thus the tribe of Benjamin would not die out, their wives would not be captured in battle, nor would they be given in marriage. The festival seems to have been a drunken orgy even if there was an element of reconciliation. If the Benjaminites wanted good stock for the future they should have heeded the advice given to the wife of Manoah (see page 113) ' . . . drink no wine or strong drink . . . you shall conceive and bear a son'. Quite apart from its effects on the woman, alcohol (even in no more than minor social indulgence) is a potent cause of physical and mental retardation in the foetus.

References

1. Wenham G.J. The Old Testament Attitude to Homosexuality. *Expository Times*. 1991, **102**: 12.

8

RUTH

The book of Ruth is a welcome relief from war and slaughter. The people in it are nice and kind to each other. For these reasons, it is worth examining, though no medical comment is called for.

A man, Elimelech, a native of Bethlehem, married Naomi. They had two sons. Because there was famine in the land the family left Bethlehem and went to Moab. The sons married Moabite women, Orpah and Ruth, but both sons died before any children were born. The food situation in Bethlehem improved, and so Naomi decided to return and Ruth, in spite of much persuasion to the contrary, insisted on accompanying her.

The two women arrived in Bethlehem at the beginning of the barley harvest and Ruth gleaned in the field owned by Boaz, a relative of Elimelech. Boaz was attracted to her and gave her preferential treatment. Naomi advised Ruth to wash and anoint herself, put on her best clothes and go down to the threshing floor where Boaz would be sleeping that night. When she found him she was to lie at his feet. Ruth did as her mother-in-law had told her and when Boaz woke up at midnight she invited him 'to spread your skirt over your maidservant' (3:9). Boaz declined but next morning gave her six measures of barley.

Boaz then consulted ten elders of the city and asked another man, a closer relative of Elimelech, whether he (the relative) would buy Elimelech's field which Naomi was selling. Boaz pointed out that if the relative bought the field 'you are also buying Ruth the Moabitess' (4:5). The relative refused and suggested that Boaz buy the field himself. This he did. Ruth became his wife and the mother of Obed, the father of Jesse, who was the father of David.

The courage and determination of the women must be admired, especially when living as they were in a patriarchal society.

9

I AND II SAMUEL

The books of I and II Samuel form a continuous narrative. Much attention is paid to the exploits of David's roaming gang, which, to put it bluntly, must have terrorised the neighbourhood.

BIRTH OF SAMUEL

The circumstances of the conception of Samuel are given in some detail (I.1:12). Hannah and Peninnah were the wives of Elkanah. Peninnah had sons and daughters and taunted Hannah with her childlessness. Every year the family went to Shiloh to offer sacrifices to the Lord, and while they were there Hannah went to the temple to pray for a son. Eli, the priest, watched her as she prayed in great distress, and as her lips moved but she did not speak, he thought she was drunk. Hannah explained matters to Eli, he blessed her and she went away and, having achieved psychic calm, became pregnant. The text (I.1:24) suggests that Hannah breast-fed Samuel for longer than the usual nine months, though why she wanted to use breast-feeding as a contraceptive method (which so long as menstrual periods are suppressed is acceptably effective) seems curious.

Eventually Hannah bore a further two sons and seven daughters.

SAMUEL AND ELI

Samuel's dreams, or voice of the Lord (I.3:4), unlike most dreams contained no distortion; they showed clearly the direction of his thoughts, a passionate desire to succeed the priest, Eli. Hannah did her best to encourage him (I.1:28). Fortunately Eli's sons were worthless men, for they took the meat which should have been sacrificed to the Lord (I.2:12) and spent their time with the women who served at the entrance to the tent of meeting (I.2:22).

Israel had been defeated in battle by the Philistines and, to guard against a further defeat, the ark of the covenant was brought from Shiloh to the Israelite camp. Despite this, the Israelites were again defeated. Eli, waiting for news of the battle, feared for the safety of the ark, his heart trembled, possibly a feeling caused by a paroxysmal fibrillation which can be exacerbated by excitement (I.4:13). When he was told that the ark had been captured, he fell over backwards and broke his neck (I.4:18). This precipitation was the result of emotion acting via the autonomic nerves. The immediate cause may have been ventricular flutter, most likely because of the preceding fibrillation, massive coronary ischaemia, massive cerebral haemorrhage or rupture of an abdominal (arterio-sclerotic) aneurysm. The causes of sudden death, but not of the instantaneous drop-down sort, are many, of which coronary thrombosis or other ischaemic heart disease is the commonest. It is noteworthy in this connection that the sudden death of drivers of motor vehicles is a very rare cause of vehicular accidents. It seems that the victims have sufficient warning to enable them to stop their vehicle.

Eli's daughter-in-law, whose husband was killed in the battle, was pregnant at the time and when she heard of his death immediately went into labour. As she was dying, her women attendants said: 'Fear not, for you have borne a son' (I.4:20) – proof, if any is needed, that sons were the ultimate satisfaction of a woman's duty.

THE PHILISTINES AND THE ARK

The Philistines, who had captured the ark, took it to Ashdod (I.5:1) and housed it in the temple of their god, Dagon, next to the statue of the god. The next three mornings the statue of Dagon was found face down before the ark and on the third morning its head and arms had been cut off, which makes it almost certain that vandals had entered the house of Dagon. The inhabitants of Ashdod and its territory were then afflicted with tumours. The Hebrew 'āphālîm means tumours or swellings in the vulva or anus, from which it has been wrongly suggested that they were haemorrhoids. In the Authorised Version the word is translated as 'emerods'. When the ark was taken to Gath (I.5:8) tumours again occurred, and when it was moved on to Ekron, tumours and deaths are reported (I.5:12). The most likely diagnosis is bubonic plague. Buboes are enlarged lymphatic glands most frequently of the groin. The next most commonly affected sites are the axilla and the neck. An alternative diagnosis of *granulomata inguinale* (a sexually transmitted disease) is ruled out by the alarming number of deaths and the mention of mice as vectors (I.6:4). Any wild rodent – rats, mice, voles, shrews – can form the reservoir of plague, but rats infected from wild rodents are the usual means of transferring infection to man. The reason is that rats tend to live near man. Rats are not mentioned in the Bible. It is strange that a pastoral society should have confused two such different animals as mice and rats. The Hebrew 'akhbār is a generic term for any small rodent. Seven species of mice occur in Palestine, to which must be added fieldmice, dormice and rats. Fleas living on the rodent become infected by biting animals already infected with *Pasteurella pestis*. The bacillus multiplies in the proventriculus of the flea's stomach and eventually blockage occurs. The flea is avid for blood and goes on biting so that regurgitation occurs. Passage to man does not occur through bites, but by droplets of dried flea stomach contents (heavily contaminated with *P. pestis*). If these are inhaled into the human lung pneumonic plague (nearly always fatal) occurs. If *P. pestis* enters the human body through mucous membranes (nose, mouth) or by scratching or through other abrasions of the skin, the bubonic form of plague, less virulent, eventuates. Some strains of *P. pestis* are so virulent that minimal infection is quickly followed by death, other strains only produce occasional death in humans.

The word 'plague' derived from the Greek *plēgē* and the Latin *plaga* is used to translate the Hebrew *makkāh*, *maggēphāh* and *negha'*. The Hebrew, Greek and Latin all suggest a strike or blow and are used frequently in the Old Testament to mean a pestilence or disaster which strikes the subject suddenly. None of the plagues of Egypt which preceded the Exodus was due to infection with *P. pestis*.

Mice (or rats) are attracted by food (and are absent where food is not available to them). In spite of the Mosaic injunction to finish food on the same day that it was prepared or to destroy it by burning (Leviticus 19:5; Numbers 9:12), food must have been accessible to mice imported to Ashdod and Gath in the ark. If so, why did the Israelites not suffer from buboes? Probably, food debris was deposited in the ark by the Philistines during its journey from Ebenezer to Ashdod and already infected mice entered it when in passage. This means either that the Philistine's baggage was mice ridden or that infected rodents were frequent in the countryside.

Probably the inside of the ark was dry and dusty with flea vomit well distributed. The death of the men who looked into the ark at Bethshemesh (I.6:19) would have been due to pneumonic plague.

SAUL

Samuel (I.8:10) warned the Israelites of the perils of having a king but at their persistent request anointed Saul (I.10:1), an action which he later regretted (I.15:35). Saul was an unstable character, suffering attacks of jealousy, depression and hyperactivity. One reason is that he was unsure of himself, unable to cope with David's undoubted success and the friendship between David and Jonathan. It is important not to force a psychological explanation but he may in his prophesying (I.10:6) have shown a flight of ideas which occur in hypomania. His fear of David may have been a paranoid reaction (I.18:12) sufficient for him to want David to be removed from his presence.

Shortly afterwards, in devious trickery, Saul gave his daughter, Michal, to be David's wife (I.18:21). Before David could marry Michal, Saul said he must produce a hundred Philistine foreskins; in fact he produced two hundred (I.18:27). One shudders at how crude the killing and mutilation must have been. Saul undoubtedly hoped that David would be killed in obtaining the foreskins. Michal, who later became Palti's wife for a short time (I.25:44), was held in contempt because 'she had no child to the day of her death' (II.6:23).

Later, Saul wanted David's death (I.19:1, 20:31) and to escape this David had to flee. While in Gath, to escape the wrath of Achish, the King of Gath, David feigned madness by making marks on the doors of the gate and slobbering on his beard (I.21:13). This performance, other than to the inhabitants of Gath, is not convincing. The characteristic of madmen is not unkempt appearance but loss of contact with reality. When in hiding from Saul, David asked the Lord's advice (I.23:12) and whether by intuition or by logical thought gave himself the desired answer. Saul did not always appreciate the moral significance of his actions, as when he killed eighty-five priests and put the inhabitants of the city of Nob to the sword for giving haven to David (I.22:19). There is sufficient evidence to support the diagnosis of cyclothymic personality in which swings of moods (hyper- to hypo-mania) are sudden and extreme. It is not surprising that he found music a palliative (I.16:23). In spite of servile fear (I.28:20), in the end Saul died bravely (I.31:4; I Chronicles 10:4).

Throughout the story of Saul there is much exaggeration (a characteristic of unstable personalities). The logistical difficulties of controlling 30,000 chariots and 6000 horsemen are ignored (I.13:5), even if these were Philistine.

DAVID

The Israelites thought of themselves as being small, but the evidence for this is scanty (see pages 77, 90). Goliath's height may have gained in the telling, but as reported he was about 11 feet 9 inches (3.85 m) tall. A span is about 9 inches (23 cm) and a cubit about 22 inches (56 cm). The sight of Goliath would have been alarming. Almost certainly, he was suffering from acromegaly and gigantism. Acromegaly and gigantism are due to disease of the anterior part of the pituitary gland, which is situated in the centre of the skull and above the nose, resting in a shallow cavity in the sphenoid bone. Just in front of the pituitary gland lies the optic chiasma in which the optic nerves from the eye join and cross before going on to the brain. The importance of this is that any enlargement of the pituitary gland may cause pressure (and loss of function) on the nerves between the eye and the brain. The immediate cause of both syndromes is excessive secretion of the growth hormone by the pituitary gland. If this occurs before puberty (when the epiphysis of the bones fuse) the speed of growth of the long bones is increased. If this occurs after puberty, the very characteristic physical features of acromegaly – bulbous nose, thickening of the lips, large hands and feet, thickening greasy skin and husky voice – develop slowly. The incidence of acromegaly is about 40 per million of the general population; gigantism is very rare.

The commonest cause of increased secretion of growth hormone is a non-metastasing tumour of the pituitary known as an adenoma, and as this enlarges it presses on the optic chiasma causing various degrees of blindness. In about a quarter of the cases of pituitary adenoma bi-temporal hemianopsia occurs (blindness to one side, vision to the other side is only slightly, if at all, affected). If David stood to one side of him, Goliath would not see David or the stone slung by David.

After David won he is reported as cutting off Goliath's head (I.17:51). This must have been a most difficult operation. Even if David had found an intervertebral joint, breaking through the exostoses – ie. bony outgrowths around joints (common in acromegaly) – cutting the intervertebral ligament would have required prohibitive strength. More than likely he contented himself with scalping Goliath, which once his knife had entered the aponeurotic space (between the scalp and the skull) would have been easy. When judicial decapitation was practised in mediaeval England it required a specially weighted axe and an experienced executioner whose skull was to land the blade across the neck, unprotected by hair or clothes, as it lay on the block. To sever the head of Lord Balmerino, who was executed on Tower Hill in August 1746, the headsman had to take three blows with a specially sharpened axe.[1] Just before the French Revolution (1789), a French physician invented the eponymous guillotine, which was then available to further the aims of the Committee of Public Safety.

While chasing David and his young men, Saul went into a cave 'to cover his feet'. This is a Hebrew idiom meaning to defecate. The Revised Standard Version renders the phrase 'to relieve himself'.

Nabal refused to feed David's gang (I.25:9), but to stop a fight Abigail, his wife, did so (I.25:18). The amount of food she produced at short notice was amazingly large and very likely to be missed before long. When Abigail told Nabal (I.25:37), he seems to have had a coronary infarction and died ten days later. This is characteristic of ischaemic heart disease; 40 to 50 per cent of persons experiencing cardiac infarction die within twenty days, half the deaths occurring within two hours.

WIVES AND CONCUBINES

Saul had five sons, the best known of whom is Jonathan. Jonathan and two of the others were slain with their father at the battle on Mount Gilboa (I.31:6). The remaining two were handed over by David to the Gibeonites to be hanged (II.21:8). Jonathan had at least one son, Mephibosheth.

Possibly because of David's defection and to spite him Saul gave Michal, whom he had previously married to David (I.18:27), to Palti (I.25:44). David later reclaimed her, much to Palti's distress (II.3:16). Michal saved David's life when he was being pursued by Saul (I.19:11). She later recognised David when he brought the ark to Jerusalem (II.6:16) and came out to reprimand him for exposing himself in front of the servant girls of the household (II.6:20).

In addition to Michal, David had at least seven other wives: Ahinoam, Abigail (I.25:42), Maacah, Haggith, Abital, Eglah and Bathsheba (II.11:3). The sons born at Hebron, at one time David's capital, were Amnon by Ahinoam, Chileab by Abigail, Absalom by Maacah, Adonijah by Haggith, Shephatiah by Abital and Ithream by Eglah (II.3:2). All this is reported in factual terms in keeping with the mores of the time. Being so, it caused no offence to individuals or society. To David's credit he rescued Abigail and Ahinoam after they had been captured by the Amalekites, who had not killed them when they raided David's camp after one of his skirmishes proved unsuccessful (I.30:3, 18). He also had at least ten concubines (II.15:16). The latter were raped by Absalom, David's son (II.16:22) while he temporarily occupied David's palace during his rebellion (see page 130). There may have been more wives and concubines (II.5:13).

ARBITRATION

The most sensible, but far from humane, person to have appeared so far in the history of Israel is Abner (II.2:26). He suggested to Joab, the commander of David's 'army', that disputes should be settled by discussion rather than by slaughter. Abner, who had been commander of Saul's army, had, after Saul's death, set up Ishbosheth (Ishbaal), one of Saul's sons, in opposition to David. During this time David was at Hebron refusing to see Abner or negotiate with him unless Michal was restored to him. At David's request, Ishbosheth ordered Palti to release Michal, and accompanied by her weeping husband, she was brought to David (II.3:16). Abner met David at Hebron and then went away to discuss the future with his followers. In the meantime Joab had returned to Hebron and when he heard of Abner's visit he sent messengers after Abner to bring him back. When Abner returned he was treacherously murdered at the gates of Hebron by a jealous Joab (II.3:27).

DAVID'S LAMENT OVER JONATHAN

David's lament over Jonathan (II.1:19–27), beautiful as it is, contains to the modern eye an unfortunate phrase: 'Your love to me was wonderful, passing the love of women.' Certainly David and Jonathan were very close friends, sufficiently close for Jonathan to disobey Saul and risk his life for David (I.20:30ff.), but there is no evidence of homosexuality.

DEFORMITY OF FEET

Jonathan's son, Mephibosheth, had deformed feet (II.4:4; 9:3) attributed to the fact that his nurse, who was carrying him, fell when she was fleeing from supposed danger following the death of Saul and Jonathan on Mount Gilboa. *Talipes equinus*, in which the heel is drawn up and the toe pointed down, like a horse, is the commonest form of acquired deformity. It results from shortening of the calf muscles and may be caused by suppuration and contracture following injury to the calf. Except in most unusual circumstances it would be unilateral. The most likely explanation of Mephibosheth's crippled feet is congenital *talipes equinus varus*, in which, besides the deformity described above, the foot is twisted inwards. This is the commonest form of *talipes* and there is some evidence that it runs in families. In Mephibosheth's case the poor nurse got the blame.

TRAFFIC ACCIDENT?

There is no evident reason why Uzzah should die after touching the ark (II.6:7). Perhaps he was run over and killed by the wheels of the cart carrying the ark. After all, the oxen had stumbled and maybe Uzzah was blamed for trying to steady the cart. David's anger is the best evidence that an accident occurred. Accidents are not acts of God. All 'accidents' are due to human failure and given enough forethought are preventable (though it must be admitted that the sequence of failures may, on occasion, appear to be nearly infinite). It is more comfortable to blame someone else or something impersonal or even God. If proof of this is needed consider traffic accidents! Technological societies exist by taking risks (in sacrificing individuals). The question is what is an acceptable risk[2] for society, whose collective answer will differ very sharply from that of the individual concerned. An overall death rate of 5 per hundred persons suffering from a particular disease means that as yet unidentified people want to know whether they will be one of the five, for each of whom the risk is 100 per cent.

CAPTURE OF JERUSALEM

David's men captured Jerusalem by climbing up a water shaft (II.5:8). The city became David's capital. Nathan the prophet (II.7:3) seems to have had delusions of grandeur in approving David's proposal that the Lord should dwell in a house of cedar like the king rather than in a tent. After the Lord made it clear that he disapproved of the whole idea, the proposal to build a temple was shelved (II.5:13).

BATHSHEBA

David's roving eye for women was displayed to the full when he stole Bathsheba from her husband, Uriah the Hittite (II.11:4), and then arranged for Uriah to be killed in battle (II.11:15). By modern mores both David and Bathsheba committed adultery at first sight, but different standards prevailed then and, after all, David was king. The question arises why Bathsheba chose to take a ritual bath after menstruation in full sight of David.[3] The conception that followed was unsuccessful, as the boy who was born died after seven days (II.12:18). Bathsheba reverts to being described as Uriah's wife, possibly significant in relation to the duty of bearing sons. However, the account suggests that after seeking consolation from the Lord on the death of his son by Bathsheba (II.12:20), David had intercourse with her seven days after the birth (II.12:24), thus offending in a major way against the Mosaic code. Be that as it may, the result was the birth of Solomon.

ABSALOM

Tamar was David's daughter and Absalom's sister (their mother was Maacah) (II.13:1), and her rape by Amnon, her half-brother and David's son by Ahinoam, was incestuous and strictly contrary to Moses's edicts (see page 66). Amon had lusted after her for some time because of her beauty but after the rape threw her out of his house and presence. An extreme example of a love-hate relationship. Eventually Amnon was killed on Absalom's orders (II.13:29). The misreporting of this incident as the death of all David's sons (because they all disappeared temporarily) caused Absalom to flee for over two years (II.14:28). During this time he cut his hair only once a year. The chance of keeping it free from nits, dirt and noxious smells must have been small though unkemptness was likely to have been usual.

Later, Absalom was forgiven by David (II.14:33) and returned to court, but, not having very much to do, came under the influence of Ahithophel (II.15:31), the highly intelligent but crafty grandfather of Bathsheba. He had never forgiven David for stealing Bathsheba, however conniving she had been. So long as Absalom followed Ahithophel's advice in his military campaign to displace David, he was successful. He moved from Hebron to Jerusalem, where Ahithophel encouraged him to have intercourse (no doubt to show who was master) with the ten concubines left behind by David, who with uncharacteristic cowardice fled Jerusalem. Later, David made provision for them by confining them for life (II.20:3). Absalom then crossed the Jordan against Ahithophel's advice to destroy David's armies in the forest of Ephraim where they were waiting for him (II.18:6). Absalom's army was utterly routed, and, fleeing from the field on a mule, Absalom caught his head in the branch of a great oak and was left hanging between heaven and earth while his mule went on. Joab was told where he was and in defiance of David's orders, killed him, by piercing his heart with three darts (II.18:14). When Ahithophel found that his advice had been rejected, he hanged himself.

Amasa took longer than three days (II.20:5) to obey David's command to summon the men of Judah (apparently to fight against Sheba, who was instigating a rebellion) and this delay resulted in perfidious Joab sticking a hidden sword into his abdomen. Amasa's bowels shed on the earth (II.20:10). The pain of exposed peritoneum would have been excruciating.

POLYDACTYLY

Polydactyly (six fingers and toes on each hand and foot) is a well-recognised if uncommon congenital abnormality (II.21:20). It is due to a heterzygous gene which when it occurs has high persistence. Generations may be skipped.

MURDER AND FAMINE

No cause for the famine that afflicted the land for three years is given (II.21:1) except blood guilt on the house of Saul because he put the Gibeonites to death. As reparation the Gibeonites wanted to hang seven of Saul's sons. David handed over Saul's remaining two sons (see page 126) and the five sons of Saul's daughter, Merab, to be hanged. Hanging was by slow suspension, leading to prolonged and painful dying. He did not give the Gibeonites Jonathan's son, Mephibosheth (II.21:7), who had deformed feet.

The united armies of David were said to number 1,300,000 men, but the command structure to control such a big force is not mentioned. Probably this figure reflects the adult male population who fought as needed in small self-supporting guerrilla groups. Warfare, in some shape or form, was continuous, to which must be added the seemingly pointless hangings and the other killings. Pestilence lasting three days (see page 134) is said to have killed 70,000 men. The land was undoubtedly neglected during the fighting, and the real wonder was that organised life continued and there were sufficient men and women left to do the work.

References

1. Walpole H. Letter to Horace Mann. :*The Oxford Book of Political Anecdotes,* ed. Paul Johnson. Oxford: Oxford University Press, 1987.
2. Urquhart J., Heilmann K. *Risk Watch: The Odds of Life.* New York: Facts on File Publications, 1984.
3. Nicol G. Bathsheba, a Clever Woman? *Expository Times.* 1988, **99**: 12.

10

KINGS AND CHRONICLES

Comments on the books of Kings and Chronicles are combined because they cover much the same period of the history of Israel. The books of Kings deal with the time from the death of King David (c.961 BC) to the fall of Jerusalem in 587 BC. The books of Chronicles start with long genealogical lists summarising the history from Adam to David and then take the narrative to the return from exile in Babylon in 538 BC.

DAVID

The build-up of David, the founder of Jerusalem (II Samuel 5:6 – 10), as a cultured and kindly king falls flat at the report that he hamstrung over a thousand of Hadadezer's chariot horses and murdered 22,000 Syrians (I Chr. 18:4), committed adultery with Bathsheba at first sight (II Samuel 11:5) and contrived the killing of her husband, Uriah (II Samuel 11:15); to say nothing of the murder of Saul's descendants. The slaughter continued when 18,000 Edomites were killed (I Chr. 18:12). Maybe his reputation rests on his ability to organise.[1] Certainly he organised an extensive harem. Perhaps being successful, especially against the Philistines, breeds success.

During one of the continuing skirmishes with the Philistines, Lahmi, brother of Goliath, was killed (I Chr. 20:5), and, as his spear was like a weaver's beam, the text implies that he was big like Goliath and had six toes on each foot and six fingers on each hand (see page 131).

Following a census carried out by Joab at the instigation of David, the male population of fighting age is given as 1,100,000 for Israel and 470,000 for Judah (excluding Levites and Benjaminites) (I Chr. 21:5). Given the choice of three years of famine, three months of devastation by his foes or three days of pestilence as punishment for carrying out the census against the will of the Lord, David accepted three days of pestilence (I Chr. 21:11). As a result 70,000 persons died. No identification of the pestilence is possible, but so many deaths occurring in a short time suggests diphtheria among the possible causes. Other specific fevers, even smallpox, would act more slowly. The 'plague' was halted when David, at the behest of an angel of the Lord, a man carrying a drawn sword (see page 16), prudently offered sacrifices to the Lord on an alter which he had built on a threshing floor bought from Ornan (I. Chr. 21:18 – 27). It may be that the threshing floor had some connection with the pestilence. Rats are choosy where they live and a threshing floor with debris easy to hand with which to make nests would be very attractive.

Murine typhus (*Rickettsia mooseri*) is transmitted when the faeces of the rat flea (*Xenopsylla cheopsis*) are rubbed into abrasions or scatches on the skin or occasionally when the conjunctival or the buccal mucous membranes are contaminated. Its incidence is worldwide. Rats and other small rodents – mice, squirrels and guinea-pigs, but particularly rats – act as reservoirs. Murine typhus is the mildest of the rickettsial infections, characterised by a mild fever, starting about ten days after infection with a slight rash often difficult to see and joint pains. The mortality is low and recovery takes two to three weeks. Other rickettsial infections include Rocky Mountain spotted fever (*R. rickettsi*), fèvre boutoneuse (*R. conori*), epidemic louse borne typhus (*R. prowazeki* or *R. Canada*), of particular importance in war when populations are on the move, scrub typhus (*R. tsutsugamushi*) and Q. fever (*R. burneti*). A rash, due to haemorrhages into the skin, occurs in all rickettsioses except Q fever. Scrub typhus does not occur in the Levant.

Rickettsiae are obligatory intracellular unicellular parasites about the size of bacteria. As their name implies, they were first identified by Dr H.T. Ricketts (1871–1910) while investigating Rocky Mountain spotted fever. He died while studying typhus fever (*R. prowazeki*) in Mexico.

David, just before his death, started to prepare the materials for the temple which his son, Solomon, was to build. He did this by conscripting aliens, foreigners who were permanently resident in Israel but had no political rights (I Chr. 22:1–5). David foreshadowed Israel's present-day citizen army by arranging for 24,000 men with their own commander to serve in the army for one month until the next contingent took over (I Chr. 27:1).

DEATH OF DAVID

An excellent way of warming a cold person is to cuddle him with both subject and therapist nude. For hypothermia it may be used as a first-aid measure. Much of David's life had been spent in sexual activity, and, besides warming him, the introduction of a young girl, Abishag the Shunammite, into his bed may have been cheering (I Kgs. 1:4). Sexual intercourse did not occur. Whilst being looked after by Abishag, David's eyesight deteriorated (I Kgs. 1:23). During his decline, Adonijah, his son by Haggith, attempted to assume the throne. David was told of this by Bathsheba and announced that Solomon, his son by Bathsheba, was to be king. Zadok the priest anointed Solomon at Gihon (I Kgs. 1:39). David died at an old but unrecorded age, having united Israel and Judah.

SOLOMON

Later, Solomon refused to allow Adonijah to marry Abishag, despite Bathsheba's intervention on his behalf, because he feared (with some reason) that a rival dynasty might be started (I Kgs. 2:22). Solomon solved the problem by having Adonijah murdered (I Kgs. 2:25).

Solomon had Joab killed because he had favoured Adonijah's claims to the throne and also because Joab had treacherously murdered Abner and Amasa, 'two men more righteous and better than himself' (I Kgs. 2:32). Joab was slain before the altar (I Kgs. 2:34).

Solomon's marriage to Pharaoh's daughter is significant in showing that Egyptian influence was strong at that time.

Solomon's request in a dream for an 'understanding mind' (I Kgs. 3:9) was 'wise and discerning' (I Kgs. 3:12). Solomon established an efficient administration (I Kgs. 4:1ff.) which provided a basis for a developing culture (I Kgs. 4:20–29). he started major building projects in Jerusalem, his palace, government headquarters and, above all, the Temple. Hiram, King of Tyre, supplied the architects to draw up the plans and also some of the material while Israel furnished the labour. To obtain the necessary manpower, Solomon extended the conscription policy of David to include Israelites by birth. He raised levies of some 180,000 men, of whom 80,000 were sent to quarry stone in the hills, 30,000 were sent to Lebanon in relays of a thousand a month – they stayed there one month and had two months at home – and 70,000 were 'burden bearers' i.e. labourers. In addition there were 3200 overseers in charge of the work (I Kgs. 5:13–17). The question arises whether these compulsory labour gangs were confined to men sojourning in Israel or whether they included true born Israelites.[2] After Rehoboam had succeeded Solomon, the system was reactivated. Adoram, a civil servant under Solomon who was responsible for the organisation of the gangs, was stoned to death (I Kgs. 12:18). Accepting Joab's census (see page 134), about one-tenth of the male population was involved. Even if these figures are exaggerated, they represent a heavy burden on the community; the real cost was separation of families and domestic unhappiness. The resentment felt by the conscripts undoubtedly played a part in the split between Israel and Judah. In addition, Solomon enslaved foreign tribes to provide more labour (I Kgs. 9:21).

Silica, either as sandstone or gold-bearing quartz, is the major geological formation in the Levant. The likelihood of silicosis (fibrosis of the lung due to the effect of silica particles) in men hewing stone, especially in gold-mines, must be considered. Evidence of silicosis is reputed to have been found in one Egyptian mummy, but it is difficult to understand how this can be. The entrails and contents of the chest (the heart was preserved separately) were removed before the process of mummification began. In any case, the lungs decay very rapidly. Quartz is the most dangerous form of silica, causing progressive silicosis very quickly.

Hand tools, such as those available to Solomon's miners, produce relatively coarse dust compared with modern power-driven tools, but even so it is just possible that in a confined space sufficient small particles would be produced to be dangerous. Particles of silica less than 0.5 microns in diameter are soluble and dissolve in the lung fluids. Particles greater than 5.0 microns in diameter are coughed up in the sputum. It is the particles between 0.5 and 5.0 microns which create the deleterious effect. Desert sand is innocuous; no case of silicosis occurred in the Eighth Army in the Western Desert during the Second World War or afterwards. In Solomon's time, tuberculosis (e.g. the burning fever of Leviticus 26:16 and the wasting sickness of Isaiah 10:16) would be a major public health risk among the general population, sleeping and eating crowded together. For men working in the mines it would be a frequent and rapidly fatal disease, especially if silicosis was present. The death rate from accidents must have been appalling and the lack of comment suggests that they were regarded as a fact of 'life' – but they happened to conscripts and in any case the hazards of day-to-day living were considerable.

The casting of the bronze for the Temple was in the charge of Hiram of the tribe of Naphtali, from Tyre. He was said to be 'full of wisdom, understanding and skill for making any work in bronze' (I Kgs. 7:14). He was also able to work *inter alia* in iron (II Chr. 2:13). To cast a bronze pillar 33 feet (10.1 m) high (I Kgs. 7:15) and a bronze bowl – the Molten Sea – of 16,000 gallons (72,736 litres) capacity (I Kgs. 7:23) would have required great metallurgical ability. Bronze is an alloy of copper (70–90 per cent), zinc (1–25 per cent) and tin (1–18 per cent). Probably the bronze of Solomon's time was low in tin. Copper was available in the Jordan valley, which was a veritable land of smelters, and also south of the Dead Sea.[3] Copper ores often contain arsenic (which during smelting is given off as arsenious oxide); chronic poisoning (dermatitis and neuritis) probably affected the smelters. Many of them would also suffer from heat exhaustion and infra-red dermatitis. The presence of arsenic makes the bronze harder. Deposits of tin and zinc occurred in the Rajasthan. Some tin came from Cornwall. Solomon had finely developed entrepreneurial skills (II Chr. 1:17).

When the Temple was finished, the ark was brought into it by the priests. The poles carrying the ark (II Chr. 5:9) were so long as to be a very inefficient way of carrying weight unless used in the manner of present-day Chinese coolies springing the load up and down. The ceremony for the dedication of the Temple must have been disgusting by modern standards as so many sheep and oxen were sacrificed that they could not be counted (I Kgs. 8:5). After the sacrifices Solomon prayed to the Lord, stating that 'there is no man who does not sin' (I Kgs.

8:46) and giving a long list of afflictions, social, environmental and medical, due to sin. To conclude the ceremony Solomon sacrificed a further 22,000 oxen and 120,000 sheep.

Solomon had 700 wives (not all Israelites) and 300 concubines (I Kgs. 11:3). One thousand women raise doubts about Solomon's wisdom, especially as he built temples to foreign gods for some of them (I Kgs. 11:8). All this was in defiance of the Lord's specific instruction that the people of Israel should not marry foreigners (I Kgs. 11:2).

DIVISION OF THE KINGDOM

After Solomon's death (I Kgs. 11:43) and the short, disastrous rule of his son Rehoboam (I Kgs. 12:1 – 20), the kingdom was divided. Rehoboam continued to reign over Judah, the southern half of the kingdom, which included Jersualem, while Jeroboam became king over Israel, the northern part of the kingdom (Table 4).

JEROBOAM (ISRAEL)

Jeroboam (I Kgs. 12:25) distinguished himself by setting up golden calves in Bethel and Dan so that his people might sacrifice to them instead of going to Jerusalem, as he feared that, once in Jerusalem, they might transfer their allegiance to Rehoboam. When Jeroboam was offering sacrifices at Bethel he was challenged by a man of God. Jeroboam immediately suffered a hysterical paralysis which 'fixed' his hand (which side is not stated) in the outstretched position (I Kgs. 13:4). After the altar had been torn down, the king's hand returned to normal. This incident did not, however, deter Jeroboam from continuing to encourage the worship of pagan gods (I Kgs. 13:33).

Jeroboam instructed his wife to consult a prophet, Ahijah, about the health of his son Abijah (I Kgs. 14:1). She was told that Abijah would die when she returned home and that all

Table 4. Kings of the divided kingdom
(The dates are approximate)

Northern kingdom Israel		Southern kingdom Judah	
Jeroboam	922 – 901 BC	Rehoboam	922 – 915 BC
		Abijam (Abijah)	915 – 913
Nadab	901 – 900	Asa	913 – 873
Baasha	900 – 877		
Elah	877 – 876		
Omri	876 – 869	Jehosaphat	873 – 849
Ahab	869 – 850		
Ahaziah	850 – 849		
Jehoram	849 – 842	Jehoram	849 – 842
Jehu	842 – 815	Ahaziah	842
		Athaliah	842 – 837
Jehoahaz	815 – 801	Joash	837 – 800
Jehoash	801 – 786	Amaziah	800 – 783
Jeroboam II	786 – 746	Uzziah	783 – 742
Zechariah	746 – 745		
Shallum	745		
Menahem	745 – 738	Jotham	742 – 735
Pekahiah	738 – 737		
Pekah	737 – 732	Ahaz	735 – 715
Hoshea	732 – 724		
Fall of Israel	722 BC	Hezekiah	715 – 687
		Manasseh	687 – 642
		Amon	642 – 640
		Josiah	640 – 609
		Jehoahaz	609
		Jehoiakim	609 – 598
		Jehoiachin	598 – 597
		Zedekiah	597 – 587
		Fall of Judah	587 BC

the males in Jeroboam's house would be utterly consumed
because of his sins (I Kgs. 14:10). Ahijah, the prophet, was
partially blind, probably from senile cataract because of his
age. Abijah may have died from any specific fever, no details
are given.

REHOBOAM (JUDAH)

Rehoboam, son of Solomon by an Ammonite mother, allowed the worship of pagan gods and permitted male prostitution (I Kgs. 14:24). He had eighteen wives and sixty concubines (II Chr. 11:21).

ABIJAM (JUDAH)

Abijam (Abijah) followed the example of his father and had fourteen wives, twenty-two sons and sixteen daughters (II Chr. 13:21).

ASA (JUDAH)

The statement that one million men under Zerah, the Ethiopian, attacked Asa (II Chr. 14:9) confirms the exaggeration of numbers in the Old Testament.

After Asa conquered Baasha, King of Israel, he took away all the timber and stones from Ramah, a city which Baasha had been building (II Chr. 16:6). This shows that timber and other building materials were scarce.

In his old age, Asa was diseased in his feet (I Kgs. 15:23). This is blamed on the fact that he did not seek the Lord but sought help from physicians (II Chr. 16:12). An obvious suggestion is that he may have suffered from rheumatoid arthritis, but it is implied that he died when the disease became severe (II Chr. 16:13). Diabetic gangrene is a possibility, especially as he died two years after the onset of the disease. Another suggestion is that Asa suffered from arteriosclerosis in the legs. Typically pain occurs on exercise and is relieved by rest (intermittent claudication). Gangrene of the extremities is not an infrequent sequela. A less common cause is Buerger's disease, in which arteries are closed due to inflammation of the lining (intima). A history of excessive tobacco smoking occurs in 90 per cent of cases. Asa, if he had Buerger's disease, could not have been so accused.

ELAH (ISRAEL)

The evils of alcohol are once more illustrated when Elah, King of Israel, while he was 'drinking himself drunk' was murdered by his treacherous commander, Zimri (I Kgs. 16:9). Zimri reigned for only seven days before he was deposed by Omri, but in that time he murdered all Elah's male relatives and friends (I Kgs. 16:11).

AHAB (ISRAEL)

Ahab, who ruled over Israel for twenty years, was, at times, weak and devoid of courage. Benhadad, King of Syria, with thirty-two other kings, was besieging Samaria and demanded that Ahab should give him his silver and gold and his wives and children. The story is not entirely clear, but it seems that Ahab was willing to give his silver and gold but drew the line at surrendering his wives and children. The elders of the land encouraged him to resist and eventually 232 governors of districts and 7000 people of Israel gathered to fight the armies of Syria (I Kgs. 20:1–15). Benhadad and his thirty-two cronies got drunk in their camp (I Kgs. 20:16) and the Syrian army was beaten. Benhadad attacked again in the spring and his army was again routed (I Kgs. 20:29). Benhadad escaped and persuaded Ahab to spare his life by promising restitution of the cities taken by his father from Samaria (I Kgs. 20:34).

Alcohol may well have played a part in the first defeat. A recent interesting finding is that 60 per cent of patients attending two emergency centres in the north-west of England who had been assaulted were themselves inebriated.[4] A World Health Organisation survey has shown that legal limits of blood alcohol have been exceeded in 30 to 50 per cent of drivers of motor vehicles involved in accidents. Of pedestrians involved in accidents 30 per cent have 'excess' alcohol in their blood.[5] Because of forensic convenience, too much attention is being paid to legally defined limits for blood alcohol. Diminution in critical faculties and in physical co-ordination arises even from non-intoxicating doses of alcohol. Just one glass of sherry given to subjects undergoing psychological tests affected discrimination.

Ahab married Jezebel, a princess from Tyre and a follower of Baal. A temple to Baal was erected in Samaria (I Kgs. 16:32) and Jezebel tried to make the cult of Baal the official religion of the court. Those who opposed her were persecuted (I Kgs. 18:4). The country was afflicted with a severe drought (I Kgs. 17:1) and Elijah pronounced this to be a punishment for Ahab's policy of permitting the worship of Baal. Elijah, saying that he was following the instructions of the Lord, went to lodge in the house of a widow living in Zarephath. She, living in the midst of drought and famine, had very little food. Elijah's presence made the shortage worse (I Kgs. 17:12). The son of the widow became ill so that there was 'no breath left in him' and he was thought to be dead (I Kgs. 17:17). Elijah laid the boy on his bed and he recovered. The most likely explanation is that the boy had fainted from inanition. In severe faints or syncope (see page 231) the pulse may be difficult to feel and breathing imperceptible. In extreme cases, unconsciousness may be prolonged (see page 232), during which time the heartbeats and respiration, even if imperceptible, must be adequate to keep the brain supplied with oxygen. No treatment except laying the patient supine is necessary. Elijah's action in laying the boy on his bed (apparently he was being held against his mother's bosom (I Kgs. 17:19), which implies some degree of uprightness) was sufficient to ensure recovery.

Ahab wanted to purchase Naboth's vineyard, which was next to his palace in the city of Jezreel, but Naboth refused to sell (I Kgs. 21:1–3). Jezebel, by lies and treachery (I Kgs. 21:8–14), succeeded in getting Naboth stoned to death and his two sons murdered. Coming face to face with Ahab in his ill-gotten vineyard, Elijah denounced this iniquity and prophesied the end of the house of Ahab and the death of Jezebel (see page 149).

Nothing in Ahab's life became him like the leaving of it. He was mortally wounded in a battle against the Syrians but he made his charioteer prop him up in his chariot facing the enemy. He died at sunset with the blood of his wound flowing into the bottom of the chariot (I Kgs. 22:35).

AHAZIAH (ISRAEL)

Ahaziah, who succeeded Ahab, and reigned for just over a year, fell from his upper window (II Kgs. 1:2) and very probably sustained a paraplegia due to a fracture of the cervical spine. Death would have ensued from broncho-pneumonia or urinary infection. Ahaziah's window is specifically said to have been a lattice, which suggests that he was careless.

Ahaziah sent messengers to enquire of Baal-zebub, the god of Ekron, whether he would recover, but they were intercepted by Elijah, who told them that the king would die because he had sent to Baal-zebub to ask about the possibility of recovery and not to the God of Israel (II Kgs. 1:6). Ahaziah then despatched his captains to fetch Elijah, who was sitting on top of a hill. The first two captains, with their accompanying detachments of fifty men, were burnt up by fire as they approached Elijah. The third captain, who with his troop no doubt obeyed orders only in fear of a worse fate, was luckier. The fire may have been lightning (II Kgs. 1:9–14). Why Elijah was not burnt is not explained, but the story is likely to have been a myth designed to ascribe magical faculties to Elijah; probably Elijah's correct forecast of the outcome of Ahaziah's fall arose from observing similar incidents.

JEHORAM (JUDAH)

Elijah did not confine himself to censuring the Kings of Israel, for in a letter to Jehoram, Elijah reproved him because he had forsaken the ways of the Lord and also murdered his brothers, who were better men than himself (II Chr. 21:13). He was told that as a consequence he would lose his wife, children and possessions and that he himself would suffer from severe sickness and an incurable disease of the bowels (II Chr. 21:15, 18). Probably the latter is an afterthought by the Chronicler to show how clever Elijah was. The symptom described is that his bowels came out day by day. Prolapsed haemorrhoids (piles) or polyp of the rectum might be considered. Amoebic dysentery due to infection with *Entamoeba histolytica* (amoebae carried in food and water, the spread of which is facilitated by poor hygiene) and the likelihood of an amoebic disease of the liver is one probability. Another is cancer of the rectum in which, due to venous obstruction, prolapse of haemorrhoids may occur and periods of diarrhoea (especially morning diarrhoea) alternate with periods of constipation. A perianal granuloma in Crohn's disease (in which ulcers due to granulomatous infiltration of the mucous membrane develop anywhere in the gastro-intestinal tract but commonly in the colon) may mimic prolapse of the anus and rectum, is possible but unlikely. Crohn's disease is uncommon, especially so in the tropics (though Palestine is north of the tropic of Cancer) where the malabsorption syndrome (sprue) may be associated with diarrhoea. The favoured diagnoses are cancer of the rectum or amoebic dystentery.

ELISHA – (THE PROPHET)

Soon after the death of Jehoram (Israel), Elijah was taken up by a whirlwind into heaven and his role as prophet was passed on to Elisha (II Kgs. 2:9 – 12).

To the Israelites (and for that matter to generations of men and women who lived when the kitchen table served as a funeral bier) death was an anticipated event: in a sense it was part of the ritual of living. To the commonplace was added the belief in the continuity of life in this world and the next and this belief was the basis of the final conversation between Elijah and Elisha. During the tempest which caught Elijah and Elisha in the open, the latter's imagination magnified the electric storm (which can be most alarming) into fire and in the confusion the pair were separated. Fire is the only thing which purifies without itself being polluted and as such is venerated by the Parsees. As such too, it is an appropriate accompaniment to death.

Elisha's first problem was to improve the water supply of Jericho. He added salt to the spring (II Kgs. 2:21). This would remove temporary hardness but would have little or no effect on the water's bacterial content. Vegetable debris, larvae and even frogs might precipitate to the bottom. For this to happen, a much higher concentration of salt than one bowl to a spring would be needed. Elisha's efforts are to be applauded, as contaminated water is the single greatest cause of death in the world.

When the combined armies of Israel, Judah and Edom had been marching in the desert for seven days, they were unable to find water (II Kgs. 3:9) (see page 34). Elisha was asked for his help, and being prompted by music to a numinous mood (something that music is supposed to do in church but does not because the hymns are so terrible) prophesied that a dried-up stream would become full of water. Once more the water is described as red as blood (II Kgs. 3:22). It seems strange that the Moabites, like the Egyptians (see page 28), were deceived by the reflection of sun in a river carrying fine particles of sand after a recent storm.

Elisha, accompanied by his servant Gehazi, was making one of his regular visits to an infertile Shunammite woman when he promised her that she would bear a son in spite of her husband's age (II Kgs. 4:16). Though Gehazi, whose probity has been questioned previously because he accepted gifts from Naaman (see page 54), was present at the Shunammite woman's house, Elisha must be the prime suspect as father of her child (II Kgs. 4:17). Though married, she urged Elisha to stop and eat food whenever he passed that way. She was sufficiently wealthy to build, with the agreement of her husband, a small extension to her home and to furnish it with a bed, table, chair and lamp so that Elisha might use it. One day, when he was staying there, Elisha asked Gehazi (who apparently was acting as interpreter) to enquire of the woman what she wanted as she had done so much for him. The reply was that she had no son and her husband was old. Elisha asked Gehazi to call the woman and told her while she was standing in the doorway that she would have a son (II Kgs. 4:16). After asking Elisha not to 'lie to your maidservant', the woman conceived and bore a son the next spring.

When the child was at an age which is not stated, but was probably late childhood or early adolescence, he was helping the reapers in his putative father's field when he complained of a severe headache and was carried indoors (II Kgs. 4:18). After some minutes on his mother's lap he is said to have died and was laid on a bed. He suffered from mild heatstroke or exhaustion; for the child to have lain on his mother's lap, even if only his head was on her lap, is bad treatment as further heat would be supplied. His mother probably gave him something to drink before he was 'dead'. If the drink contained salt, so much the better. Clearly the boy had not died and when Elisha arrived he did no more than rouse him from a deep sleep. By placing his mouth to the boy's, Elisha may have thought he was breathing life into him (II Kgs. 4:32–34). The 'kiss of life' had not then been invented. Artificial respiration in these conditions would have been entirely pointless and perhaps harmful as creating more heat. The boy should have been stripped naked, laid on a 'charpoy' bed and cooled as quickly as possible. This is most easily done by throwing cold water over the patient.

Elisha also saved a group of prophets from death by poisoning (II Kgs. 4:38–41). He was at Gilgal where there was famine in the land and one of the prophets went out into the fields to gather herbs for some sort of vegetable broth. The prophet picked gourds from a wild vine and cut them up into the broth, not knowing what they were. The gourds were undoubtedly the fruit of *Citrullus colcynthis*, which grows in profusion around Gilgal and whose fruits could be mistaken for melons. The fruit contains an extremely potent cathartic, the fatal dose of which may be as low as 15 g. The 'vine of Sodom' (Deuteronomy 32:32) is probably the same plant. The prophets realised that there was something wrong – 'there is death in the pot' (II Kgs. 4:40) – as soon as they tasted the bitterness in the broth. Elisha threw meal, probably wheat or barley flour, into the broth; this would absorb the toxin and fall to the bottom of the pot and the liquid on top could then be poured out and eaten safely.

Twice, Elisha roused the conscience of misers. First, when neighbours gave oil to the widow who was pursued by creditors (II Kgs. 4:1) and secondly when the hundred men, besides supposedly feeding on twenty loaves and some grain, supplemented this with their equivalent of packed lunches (II Kgs. 4:42).

Elisha's encounter with Naaman (II Kgs. 5:8) is very important in distinguishing between ṣāra'ath and myco-bacterial leprosy (see page 49). The ostracism to which lepers were subject is well illustrated by the story of the four lepers outside the gate of Samaria (II Kgs. 7:3–10). Even though the lepers saved the city, they do not seem to have been admitted. A stampede of the populace looting the Syrian camp to obtain food followed. During this a guard at the gate of Samaria was trampled to death (II Kgs. 7:17). While Samaria was besieged, a child is said to have been boiled and eaten (II Kgs. 6:28–30). If this is true, cannibalism being the grossest insult to the deepest taboos, psychiatric symptoms would undoubtedly have followed.

When Elisha was in Damascus, Benhadad of Syria sent Hazael to him to ask if he would recover from his illness (II Kgs. 8:7). Elisha assured Hazael that Benhadad would recover but added that Hazael would be the next King of Syria. Hazael returned and murdered Benhadad the next day by smothering him with a wet coverlet (II Kgs. 8:15). This seems a dirty trick even though it saved Benhadad anxiety about dying and fulfilled Elisha's prophecy. Hazael would have had to use force far beyond just laying the wetted cloth over Benhadad's face.

Elisha died in the reign of Jehoash of Israel. Before his death, Elisha made Jehoash shoot arrows through a window to signify his forthcoming victory over the Syrians (II Kgs. 13:14). Elisha's miracles continued after his death. When a marauding band of Moabites suddenly appeared, a man who was being buried was thrown into Elisha's tomb and is said to have come alive; if there was a miraculous event this was due to the man's sheer terror of being buried alive (II Kgs. 13:21).

JEHU (ISRAEL)

Eventually the people of Israel rebelled against the house of Ahab. Elisha brought matters to a head when he summoned one of the 'sons of the prophets' to anoint Jehu as King of Israel (II Kgs. 9:1–13). Jehu came to Jezreel, where he found Jehoram, the king, accompanied by Ahaziah of Judah, who had come to visit him. Jehoram drove out to meet Jehu, but Jehu drew his bow and shot Jehoram through the heart; Ahaziah was also shot down as he fled (II Kgs. 9:24, 27).

Jehu's most spectacular murder was that of Jezebel (II Kgs. 9:30–37) (see page 144). When she realised that she was about to be killed, Jezebel painted her eyes and adorned her head, as befitted a king's daughter. She looked out of her window at Jehu and he commanded her eunuchs to hurl her down. She was trampled to death by the horses and all her body except her hands, her feet and her skull was eaten by dogs: this saved Jehu the worry of her having an identifiable grave. Jehu completed his bloodbath by having the seventy sons of Ahab decapitated, thus removing all possible claimants to the throne (II Kgs. 10:7).

Jehu eliminated the worship of Baal by enticing all the worshippers into their temple on the pretext that he was going to offer sacrifices to Baal. Once they were inside he butchered them all. The temple was then demolished and a latrine was erected on the site (II Kgs. 10:18 – 27).

ATHALIAH (JUDAH)

When Athaliah, widow of Jehoram, heard that her son, Ahaziah, had been murdered by Jehu (II Kgs. 9:27), she seized the throne and put to death all the members of the royal family who might oppose her (II Kgs. 11:1). Joash, the infant son of Ahaziah, escaped the purge as he was hidden by his aunt Jehosheba (II Kgs. 11:2). She was the wife of Jehoiada, the priest, who seven years later incited the army to mutiny (II Kgs. 11:4 – 21). Athaliah was slain at the horse gate of the king's house (II Chr. 23:15) and Joash, now aged 7, was placed on the throne (II Kgs. 11:21).

JOASH (JUDAH)

Joash reigned for forty years and while Jehoiada, the priest, was alive he was a good king. After Jehoiada's death, his son Zechariah became priest in his place and he rebuked the people because they had forsaken the commandments of the Lord. Joash, forgetting the kindness which Jehoiada, Zechariah's father, had shown him, ordered Zechariah to

be stoned to death (II Chr. 24:22). Later that year the
Syrians attacked Judah, and Joash was severely wounded
in the battle. His servants 'conspired against him because
of the blood of the son of Jehoiada the priest and slew him
on his bed' (II Chr. 24:25).

UZZIAH (JUDAH)

Uzziah was smitten with ṣāra'ath because he usurped
the authority of the priests and burned incense before the
Lord (II Chr. 26:16–21) (see page 53). He seems to have
been a good king, so probably attracting the envy of the
less able, doing what was right in the eyes of the Lord
and undertaking useful public work, though he permitted
the worship of Baal to continue.

MENAHEM (ISRAEL)

Menahem started his reign by killing Shallum, son of Jabesh
(II Kgs. 15:14), and then went on to sack Tappuah, where
he 'ripped up' all the pregnant women, who consequently
suffered a very painful death from exposure of the peritoneum
(II Kgs. 15:16). He was not smitten with ṣāra'ath.
Comparison of the actions of Uzziah and Menahem disposes
of the fiction that ṣāra'ath is the result of sin.

FALL OF THE KINGDOM OF ISRAEL

The northern kingdom was conquered in 722 BC by Assyria
(geographically approximating to northern Iraq), and the
incorporation of Israel into the Assyrian empire resulted
in a mix of populations (II Kgs. 17:24). The foreigners
continued to worship their own gods and to follow their
pagan practices including child sacrifice (II Kgs. 17:31). The
story of the northern kingdom of Israel stops at this point.

AHAZ (JUDAH)

The worship of pagan gods continued to be allowed in Judah and Ahaz burnt his son as a sacrifice (II Kgs. 16:3).

HEZEKIAH (JUDAH)

Judah at this time was forced to pay tribute to Assyria. Hezekiah constructed a water tunnel (II Kgs. 20:20, II Chr. 32:30) from the Kidron springs (just outside the walls of Jerusalem) to the pool of Siloam to ensure the water supply of the city in the event of a siege by the Assyrians. The quality of the water may have been dubious. Rats infesting the tunnel with the consequent risk of Weil's disease (see page 78) would have been only one of the hazards. The expected siege took place and Rabshakeh, the emissary of Sennacherib, King of Assyria, accused Hezekiah of relying on the questionable help of Egypt (which was anxious to reassert its authority in the area). He said that this reliance was ill-founded and that the besieged population would be forced to eat its own dung and drink its own urine (II Kgs. 18:19 – 27). Lunatics may very rarely eat their own excreta, but there is no report of sane men doing this however hungry. Rabshakeh offered peace with the promise that every man would have his own vine, his own fig tree and his own cistern, water being so important.

Reputedly, Jerusalem was delivered from Sennacherib by a catastrophe which killed 185,000 Assyrians overnight while they were camped outside the city (II Kgs. 19:35). No obvious explanation exists for this disaster. A large number of fit men, who the previous day were engaged in military duties, seem to have died in a few hours. Death from plague, even if pneumonic, would not be so quick. If cholera was the cause, a common source of infected water would be needed, and a similar argument about common food would apply to botulism. Both plague and cholera can be ruled out as the

Israelites were not affected. The text suggests that some men survived, even if only Sennacherib (II Kgs. 19:36). The army would live on the country – food that year was what grows of itself (II Kgs. 19:29) – and the men would be messing in small groups. Poisoning by toadstools or berries eaten by the more enterprising messes is the most likely explanation. The corpses were outside the city and unless disposed of in a sanitary way – and there is no record that they were – would create a major health hazard. The sky would have been black with vultures: there is no record of this. A more likely explanation is that a small mess of men died from some form of poisoning. As there was no obvious cause for their death, the Assyrian army panicked and decamped. The few corpses found by the Israelites were exaggerated in the telling to a massacre, allowing much boasting that an angel of the Lord was on their side. Another, more mundane explanation, is that the Assyrian army marched away to deal with a threatened attack in another part of the Empire.

Isaiah (see page 168) cured Hezekiah – or rather brought him back from imminent death – by applying a poultice of figs to his boil (II Kgs. 20:1–7). Presumably the boil then burst and discharged pus, thus relieving the toxaemia. Anything will do as a poultice so long as it retains heat; mashed up figs would be entirely suitable. Bread and linseed meal were the favourites before the discovery of antibiotics eliminated the use of poultices. It is surprising how often, and for how long, boils remain unnoticed. Lack of daily washing and failure to strip the patient naked during a medical examination are contributory factors, the latter is especially liable to occur if the patient is royal.

MANASSEH (JUDAH)

Manasseh was a nasty piece of work, spoilt by being king from the age of 12 (II Kgs. 21:1). Not only did he rebuild the alien places of worship destroyed by his father, Hezekiah, but he built altars to Baal and other pagan gods. Worse, he burnt his sons as an offering to them. When held in fetters by the Assyrians (II Chr. 33:11) he was, presumably in fear of death, converted to the Lord. While in exile Manasseh is said to have written a prayer entreating divine forgiveness for his sins (II Chr. 33:18). This has not survived. The Prayer of Manasseh in the Apocrypha was probably written some time in the second or first century BC.

His son, Amon, was no better and after two years as king was murdered by his servants.

JOSIAH (JUDAH)

The next king, Josiah, a son of Amon, was altogether different. He was only 8 years old when he succeeded his father, but in his long reign of thirty-one years he instituted a thorough religious reform. He restored the Temple and during the work discovered the book of the law of Moses – probably all or most of Deuteronomy. Worship of the Lord according to the law of Moses was re-established, the worship of Baal was prohibited, the houses of Baal were destroyed, sacrifices were limited to the Temple in Jerusalem, male prostitution was abolished and child sacrifice was outlawed (II Kgs. 23, II Chr. 34,35).

Josiah was killed at the battle of Megiddo in 609 BC, fighting against the Pharaoh Neco (II Kgs. 23:29, II Chr. 35:20–24). This was the end of Judah's independence. The kingdom remained under Egyptian domination until the Egyptians were defeated by Nebuchadnezzar, King of Babylon, at Carchemish in 605 BC. Jehoiakim, King of Judah, rebelled against Nebuchadnezzar, his new overlord, but died before Nebuchadnezzar could march against Judah. In 597 BC Nebuchadnezzar besieged Jerusalem. Jehoiachin, who had succeeded Jehoiakim, surrendered (II Kgs. 24:8–12). The king, the queen mother, the high officials and the leading citizens, together with an enormous booty, were taken to Babylon. The next king, Zedekiah, although he had been placed on the throne by Nebuchadnezzar, again rebelled against Babylon. Once more the Babylonian armies moved against Jerusalem and completed its destruction in 587 BC. Nebuchadnezzar ordered Zedekiah's sons to be slain before their father and then Zedekiah's eyes were put out and he was taken prisoner to Babylon (see page 176). Nearly all the citizens and all the treasures of the Temple were taken to Babylon. Only the poorest of the land were left as vine dressers and ploughmen (II Kgs. 25:12). Compared with the usual treatment of prisoners of war[6], the march to Babylon and the treatment and captivity of the Israelites were gentle. Thus began the exile.

References

1. Blunt A.W.F. *Israel Before Christ*. London: Oxford University Press, 1924.
2. Rainey A.F. Compulsory Labour Gangs in Ancient Israel. *Israel Exploration Journal,* 1970. **20**, 3–4.
3. Wright E.G. *Biblical Archaeology*. London: Duckworth, 1974.
4. Yates D.W., Hadfield J.M., Peters K. Alcohol consumption of patients attending two accident and emergency departments in north-west England. *Journal of the Royal Society of Medicine.* 1987, **80**: 486.
5. World Health Organisation. *Global Estimates for Health Situation Assessment and Projections (WHO/HST/90.2). Geneva, 1990.*
6. Adamson P.B. Medical Complications associated with Security and Control of Prisoners of War in the Ancient Near East. *Medical History.* 1990, 34:311.

11

EZRA AND NEHEMIAH

In 539 BC, Cyrus, King of Persia, conquered Babylon.
A year later he issued a decree permitting the Jewish
exiles to return home, commanding the rebuilding of the
Temple with financial support from the Persian treasury
and ordering the return of the Temple treasure looted by
Nebuchadnezzar (Ezra 1:2ff.). There was no great rush to
return to Jerusalem, and work on rebuilding the Temple was
suspended because of the machinations of the Samaritans.
Work was resumed eighteen years later, in 520 BC, when
Darius, then King of Persia, confirmed the decree of Cyrus
and gave further financial help to the rebuilding. The Temple
was completed in 515 BC (Ezra 6:15). The position of the
returned exiles remained insecure, with hostile neighbours,
a corrupt priesthood and inefficient administration.

In 444 BC Nehemiah, a Jew who was cupbearer to
the Persian king Artaxerxes I, was appointed Governor of
Judah. The book of Nehemiah is mainly autobiographical,
the only part of the Old Testament to be so. Nehemiah found
conditions in Judah even worse than he expected and, after a
secret midnight survey, decided that rebuilding the walls of
Jerusalem must be his first priority. Because of the continuing
hostility from the neighbouring provinces, especially from
Samaria, led by Sanballat, Nehemiah divided his labour
force into two shifts, one to stand to arms while the other
worked, and even those who worked had to carry a tool in

one hand and a weapon in the other. Nights were spent in
Jerusalem, both for the protection of the workers and so
that they might make a quick start at daybreak. Because
the people 'had a mind to work' (Neh. 4:6) the walls were
completed in fifty-two days (Neh. 6:15). Nehemiah and his
staff supervised the work and did not take off their clothes
until the walls were finished (Neh. 4:23).

Nehemiah introduced a number of economic reforms
including the remission of the taxes that former governors
had imposed for the support of themselves and their staff
(Neh. 5:14). He gave the country honest administration and
political stability.

Ezra, a Jewish scribe who in modern parlance held the
post of Minister of State for Jewish Affairs at the court
of Artaxerxes II, was commissioned by the Persian king
in 398 BC to go to Jerusalem and regularise Jewish law
and practice 'according to the law of your God which is
in your hand' (Ezra 7:14). The book which Ezra took with
him was probably all or most of the Pentateuch (the first five
books of the Old Testament) which had been worked over
and incorporated into Jewish historical tradition during the
exile. Ezra read the book to the people at a solemn ceremony
(Neh. 9:38 – 10:39). Within the framework of political stability provided by Nehemiah, the religious reforms of Ezra
ensured that henceforth the distinguishing sign of the Jewish
community would be adherence to the law of Moses.

Both Ezra and Nehemiah denounced the marriages of
Jews with Gentiles. When Nehemiah discovered that the
children of such marriages could not speak Hebrew, he
flew into a rage and, having cursed, assaulted and
pulled the beards of such offenders as were nearby,
made them swear to desist from marriage with foreigners in future (Neh. 13:23). When he found that
a grandson of the High Priest had married a daughter
of Sanballat, he drove him out of the country (Neh.
13:28).

Despite Nehemiah's efforts, mixed marriages continued and Ezra came to the conclusion that drastic action was called for. He decided not just to stop future intermarriage but to dissolve existing mixed marriages (Ezra 10:3). At an open-air meeting held in Jerusalem in the pouring rain it was agreed that a commission should be set up to examine the cases of mixed marriages. At the end of three months the commission produced a list of offenders who were to put away their foreign wives with their children (Ezra 10:44). Medically this was undesirable. The need to keep the Jews, as the chosen people of God, free from the effects of foreign influence overrode the need to refresh the genetic stock.

12

ESTHER

Including the Additions to the Book of Esther from the Apocrypha.

The book of Esther has little, if any, historical support and displays an undesirable moral tone. It was probably written in 150–100 BC to explain the origin of the Jewish feast of Purim.

The nicest person is Queen Vashti who refused to display her charms and those of her ladies before King Ahasuerus's drunken cronies (1:10ff.). To her, the resultant divorce may have been welcome. Ahasuerus then had beautiful virgins brought to him so that the one who pleased him might become queen. Among them was Esther, a cousin of Mordecai, a Jew, who held a position at the court. Before being taken to the king, Esther was beautified by having her body rubbed with myrrh (presumably in a weak alcoholic solution) for six months and anointed with spices and ointment for a further six months. The period of twelve months' quarantine was doubtless to ensure that the king was the father of any child who might subsequently be born. When Esther was taken into the king's presence, she pleased him and Ahasuerus made her his queen. She had, on the instructions of Mordecai, concealed the fact that she was a Jewess.

Mordecai had fallen out with Haman, a specially favoured courtier, and Haman, who knew that Mordecai was a Jew, decided on a fearful revenge. He persuaded the king to authorise a massacre of all the Jews in the kingdom. Mordecai urged Esther to use her influence with the king and get the order countermanded. She hesitated as the penalty for entering the king's presence without a summons was death, unless the king was moved to hold out his golden sceptre to the intruder. Mordecai reminded Esther that the risk was worth taking, for if nothing was done she, together with all the other Jews, would be killed anyway. When she appeared before the king, he looked fiercely upon her and she fainted. The king was greatly agitated and when she recovered he promised to grant her anything she asked. She invited the king and Haman to a banquet at which she admitted that she was a Jewess and begged the king to cancel Haman's order. As a result of her intervention the massacre of the Jews was halted and Haman was hanged on the gallows he had prepared for Mordecai. Alas, Esther also asked that the Jews should be allowed to avenge themselves on their enemies. There was a terrible killing and the Jews slaughtered 75,500 persons living in Susa and the provinces. The dead included the ten sons of Haman who were hanged (see page 131) like their father.

The book has no medical significance except to confirm Sigmund Freud's (see page 245) emphasis on the power of the sexual drive.

13

JOB

Whether or not Job was a historical person, his story, like that of Hamlet, shows great insight into the human mind. Job owned 7000 sheep, 3000 camels, 500 yoke of oxen and 500 she-asses. He is described as 'the greatest of all the people of the east' (1:3). With such riches he had a position in society to keep up. His success seems to have attracted opprobium and envy (1:10). He fathered seven sons and three daughters (1:2). Certainly, Job took his family responsibilities very seriously, and his anxieties about whether or not his children had contravened the Mosaic law are likely to have been the cause of a breakdown in an obsessive personality. A guess may be made that Job had been brought up as a child in a frugal family much concerned with religious observance of an authoritarian nature. The daily extravagant feasts of his sons (to which his daughters were invited) concerned Job. To make retribution to the Lord, Job offered frequent burnt offerings (1:5). Yahweh was just, Job could believe nothing else, but nevertheless Yahweh was both prosecutor (of those who sinned against him) and judge.[1] Job worried that in these circumstances he might not be judged justly.

Job's pre-morbid personality would have made him a member of that large group of people in society who, living apparently normal lives, suffer from psychiatric symptoms sufficient to worry them. Population studies to determine the incidence of neuroses are bedevilled by taxonomy. This difficulty is avoided in a survey carried out in Harlow[2] in the early 1960s when the number of people consulting their medical practitioners was determined. In one year, for every thousand persons, two would be in a mental hospital, six to eight attending psychiatric out-patient clinics and forty to fifty under the care of their general practitioner for overt psychiatric illness. In addition some hundred to two hundred and fifty persons would suffer symptoms of psychological origin which were significant to themselves.

Obsessive persons tend to show two characteristics: retreat to compulsive ritual and to uncertainty. Job performed ritual sacrifices and indulged in almost endless soliloquies about justice and divine purpose.

Job's wife was remarkably loyal to him, and like most wives knew more about her husband than he did himself. 'Do you still hold fast your integrity?' (2:9).

After suffering apparent material loss and the reported death of his sons and daughters when his eldest son's house collapsed, Job did not 'charge God with wrong' (1:22) but endured much torment from disease, the physical manifestation of which was concentrated in his skin. Suggested diseases listed by Kahn[3] include leprosy, cutaneous smallpox, dermatitis herpetiformis, syphilis (which suggestion came from the USA, but of course, in Job's time it had not escaped from the New World), scurvy, pellagra, erysipelas and chronic eczema. The inclusion of leprosy, suggested in 1887,[4] is interesting; for reasons explained on page 46 this would be ṣāra'ath, a neuro-dermatitis resulting from psychiatric stress, and not mycobacterial leprosy. Guy[5] is in no doubt that Job's illness was psychosomatic.

Job believed himself to be 'a just and blameless man' and was hurt by the thought that he might be a laughing-stock (12:4). Certainly, Job was highly obsessive and his mental processes have been subject to psychological analyses for many years. Kahn[3] has reduced these to manageable proportions. Being so miserable saved Job from facing the realities of the world. The life of a righteous man is fraught with difficulty, having to accept a society whose standards fall below what he thinks they should be and refusing to accept these standards for himself. Job's wife seems to have been irritated with his attitude to his skin afflictions, which, whatever they may have been, were not made better by his self-blaming misery or by washing in lye (see page 95) and snow (9:30).

Job's friends, Eliphaz, Bildad and Zophar, were very loyal in the comfort they tried to bring him, and it was not until Elihu, a younger friend, lost his temper with the other three and with Job (32:2) that any improvement occurred. The Lord spoke to Job out of a whirlwind telling him to gird up his loins 'like a man' (38:3) and then declared to him the wonders of creation and the insignificance of man compared with them. Job accepted that he had 'uttered what I did not understand' and repented in dust and ashes. Small thanks did Eliphaz, Bildad and Zophar get for their efforts, however well intentioned these were. The Lord dismissed them 'as folly' and commanded the three to offer sacrifices (42:7).

Perhaps Job was like John Jeffreys, whose memorial in Ely Cathedral reads:

'John Jeffreys died 1763. Who lived with inflexible constancy, commendable integrity and died with an unblemished character. 27th January 1763 aged 48.'

Obsession is impelled by ever-increasing standards and by relying on perfection in ritual. Job may have felt that his bad fortune was the loss of the good fortune to which he was entitled. Undoubtedly Job's obsession had endogenous and reactive elements. Without apparent reasons, symptoms may remit.

Note: The copy of Risdon Bennett's[4] book *The Diseases of the Bible* (1887) held in the library of the Royal Society of Medicine was presented by the late Dr George Todd in 1935. It was supplied by Andrew Iredale, bookseller, Fleet Street, Torquay. A pencil note reads: 'Job's disease; he recovered and had three daughters most beautiful in the land and lived to 140!' Todd's first appointment in 1881 was Medical Officer to Brigg Urban District. In 1894 he moved to Torquay and held appointments at a number of nursing-homes.[6]

References

1. Jung C.G. *Answer to Job.* London: Routledge and Kegan Paul, 1954.
2. Taylor (Lord), Chave S. *Mental Health and Environment.* London: Longmans Green, 1964
3. Kahn J.H. *Job's Illness.* Oxford: Pergamon Press, 1970.
4. Risdon Bennett J. *The Diseases of the Bible.* London: Religious Tract Society, 1887.
5. Guy W. Psychosomatic dermatology circa 400 BC. *Archives of Dermatology and Syphilology.* 1955, **71**: 354.
6. Bolt M. – personal communication, 1984.

14

THE PSALMS

The Psalms are poems, written by many poets at many different dates. They must be read as poems with all the emotional rather than logical connotations which are proper to lyric poetry. They often express highly introspective thoughts, revealing the author's hopes and fears in simile, metaphor and allegory.

Lack of teeth would have been a serious disability, but the reference to 'break the teeth' must be read metaphorically (Psalm 3:7). The Israelites would not have been free from dental caries despite the fact that sugary agents were virtually restricted to honey and sweet resins. Many persons would have worn their teeth down by eating agricultural products contaminated with sand; sheep do this very commonly. Psalm 102 is a catalogue of psychosomatic symptoms. Psalm 109 expresses many unfulfilled wishes culminating in the unworthy thought (109:13) 'may his name be blotted out in the second generation' which was the constant fear of all Israelites. The same wish appears in Psalms 9:5 and 41:5, repeating the overwhelming fear of not living on in one's children (see page 10).

Many of the Psalms reinforce the ideas of the Old Testament: sickness is the result of sin (Psalms 35:13, 107:17), wounds fester because of foolishness (Psalm 38:5), anxiety causes unsoundness of flesh (Psalm 38:7). In Psalm 51:4 David admits that he has sinned: perhaps he remembers his offence against Bathsheba and asks forgiveness. Procreation is a sin (Psalm 51:5), but that does not seem to have worried anyone very much. Wickedness is thought to be genetic, whereas in fact behaviour, whether wicked and cruel or good and kind, is culturally determined. Children, like dogs, reflect the example of parents or owners.

Poisoned quails reappear in Psalm 78:30 (see page 75), as do the plagues of Egypt (Psalms 78:44, 105:30, 135:8) (see page 27). Psalm 78 is an account of Moses's exploits in the desert. Adolescent loss of self-esteem accounts for the anxiety expressed in Psalm 88:15, schizophrenia cannot be excluded. Figure 3 (see page 21) shows that the attainment of the ages of 70 and 80 years (Psalm 90:10) would be exceptional.

Fortunately, allegory saves him 'who abides in the shadow of the Almighty' (Psalm 91:1) from the dire consequences of treading 'on the lion and the adder' (91:13). In the Garden of Eden, between the Tigris and the Euphrates rivers, the serpent had already acquired a reputation for subtlety (Genesis 3:1). Provided that they are not frightened, snakes do not usually attack. Medically important snakes have one or more fangs in the mouth (usually at the front) which inject venomous toxins. Bites of the European adder do not cause death except in a debilitated child, though severe local symptoms may occur. Adders live in crevices, burrows and holes in the earth (nowadays commonly in field drains). It is unlikely that the snakes in the Garden of Eden (part of what is now Iraq) were confined to adders. Cobras, kraits and vipers are also likely to have been present. Indeed, the Hebrew *pethen* is translated as 'cobra' or 'asp' (a small venomous hooded snake found in Egypt). Cleopatra is said to have died after encouraging an asp to bite her following Mark Antony's defeat and death. Whether the Israelites distinguished these from adders is not clear from the biblical texts, and adders may have been a generic term for snakes. Most snake bites occur in farms, long grass and scrub. The feet and lower limbs are the common sites. Often the snake is trodden on at night. This would almost certainly guarantee a bite.

Alcohol, by depressing the mental and physiological centres of the brain, thereby lessening anxiety and interpersonal reserve, gladdens the heart of man (Psalm 104:15). Judgement (and execution of muscular actions) becomes blurred.

Psalm 106:28 refers to the fraternisation with Moabite women (see page 86) resulting in the fear of diluting genetic stock (see page 67). Moab, which was the territory east of the Jordan, is described as a washbasin (Psalm 108:9).

Psalm 144:1 thanks the Lord for training hands and fingers for war and battle.

Psalm 128:3 compares the fecund wife with a fruitful vine and goes on to hope that grandchildren will be known to one (128:6). The coals of Psalm 140:10 were charcoal, possibly supplemented by bitumen from the occasional deposit near the Dead Sea.

The Lord is right-handed (Psalms 44:3, 98:1).

15

ISAIAH

FUTURE BLESSINGS

The three or more unknown authors of Isaiah enjoy
thundering about the ills which have befallen and will
continue to befall the men, women and children of Israel
because they have rebelled against the Lord. Whether they
enjoyed counting the blessings which would be Israel's
when the ways of the Lord prevailed is another matter.
Chapter 11 is a picture of peace in the land: 'The wolf
shall dwell with the lamb, and the leopard shall lie down
with the kid' (11:6). The most cursory reading of Joshua,
Judges, I and II Samuel or even I and II Kings will show
how attractive this idea would be, but nature thrives on
competition.

ONE MAN

Seven women supplicating one man (4:1) reflects not only
the shortage of men following the destruction of Judah,
but the culturally induced shame felt at the prospect of not
having a child (see page 10). A similar sentiment is expressed
in 23:4.

PUNISHMENT

For centuries, tuberculosis (infection with *Bacillus tubercule*) has been known as the wasting sickness (10:16). Pulmonary tuberculosis is spread from person to person in droplets derived from the sputum. Nearly always this is due to the human bacillus. The bovine bacillus is usually transmitted by eating infected milk or meat and the infection tends to concentrate in the small gut, kidneys and abdominal glands. The king's evil, scrofula, of mediaeval times was tuberculosis, usually involving infection of the lymphatic glands of the neck (or one side of the neck) with the bovine bacillus. There is no organ of the body which, on occasion, cannot be infected with the tubercule bacillus.

The drying-up of the Nile (19:5) is a threat which, if it came about, would devastate Egypt. The failure of the harvest would result in widespread famine as in Pharaoh's time (Genesis 41:54).

BYSSINOSIS

Operatives exposed to the dust of flax and cotton (19:9), and for that matter hemp and jute, will, in the absence of exhaust ventilation or other means of controlling dust such as wetting, suffer from byssinosis. Byssinosis is characterised by tightening of the chest (often worse when returning to work after an absence); attacks of coughing and breathlessness supervene until total pulmonary disability ensues. Of the processes involved in the production of linen (flax) or cotton cloth, the dustiest is combing (carding) the matted fibres to make them lie the same way. For this reason carders are the prime candidates for byssinosis, but workers on all processes may be affected. By the time cotton is white, most of the dust has been removed, and weavers, though affected, are less troubled than workers in earlier processes. The technological means of keeping the airborne dust concentrations below 200 microns per cu. cm of air would not have been available to the Egyptians. Workers in combed flax and cotton are rightly described as 'in despair'. Their life expectancy would be short.

NAKEDNESS

Isaiah, the son of Amoz, walked naked and barefoot for three years (20:3) as a sign that the King of Assyria would lead captives from Egypt and Ethiopia naked and barefoot, with buttocks uncovered, 'to the shame of Egypt' (20:4). Covering of the pudenda is a subject that has been neglected by anthropologists. Children do not show shame at exposure but acquire inhibitions which may be so severe as to disturb the psychosexual life.

STAMMERING

Speech needs a very high degree of neurone integration in the brain. The centre for speech is the left side of the cerebrum in the occipital lobe. Stammering (32:4) nearly always starts during the intensive speech acquisition, normally during the third and fourth years of age. Some people find speaking in public (e.g. reading aloud at school) stressful and may develop a stammer. Anxiety may play a part, but to regard this as a major factor is wrong. Children do not 'grow out' of stammering, and treatment should be started at the earliest possible moment.

UTOPIA

After dire warnings about the vengeance of the Lord the prophet promises safety and joy to the chosen people. In this Utopia 'no inhabitant will say "I am sick" and the people who dwell there will be forgiven their iniquity' (33:24). In the prophet's mind, sickness was equated with sin. Many

high falutin' words have been written on health: an essential
ingredient in any definition is provided by the second collect
at Matins 'whose service is perfect freedom'.

SLAUGHTER BY ANGEL

There is a reference to the death of 185,000 Assyrians, the
greater part of the army of Sennacherib, when they were
encamped outside Jerusalem. As in II Kings (see page 152),
these deaths are attributed to the action of 'the angel of the
Lord' (37:36).

GILDING

The ark of the Lord was made from acacia wood (Exodus
37:1) which was overlaid with gold. Mediaeval craftsmen
used an amalgam of gold (or silver) with mercury to paint the
surface to be gilded (or silvered) before applying the leaf. The
mercury was driven off by heat, ensuring that the workmen,
almost without exception, were poisoned. Mercury and its
salts do not appear to have been available to the Israelites;
some other bonding material from a vegetable source or even
egg-white may have been used (40:19). The Israelites had
access to tin and lead, so that it is reasonable to assume that
they were able to join metals by soldering. Their problem
was that, even if the soldering was said to be good, it had
to be reinforced with rivets (nails) (41:7). Probably the
flux used for the final degreasing was of vegetable origin.
Importantly, the previous verse (41:6) says: 'Every one helps
his neighbour.'

IRON

Water again comes to the fore (41:17) and the ironsmith who
does not drink becomes faint (44:12). Syndromes caused by
heat are discussed on page 34. The coals over which the

ironsmith worked and which were used to bake bread (44:19, 54:16) were charcoal. In 60:17 iron was valuable, even if previously the Philistines provided and worked it.

BIRTH OF A NATION

In verses 47:1ff. the dislike and contempt for Babylon (of which the Chaldeans were the first settlers) are symbolised by a virgin who 'suffered a fate worse than death' and was then afflicted with widowhood and death.

The soil of Judah must have been chalky in places as flints are mentioned (50:7). A flint was indeed used by Zipporah to circumcise Moses's son (see page 17). In verse 52:1 circumcision is used to distinguish the 'clean' from the 'unclean'. Antimony, not found in the Levant, is mentioned in 54:11. Carbuncles (54:12) are red stones often engraved for signets.

The birth of a nation, which takes time and must be in due order, is likened to the birth of a child, which also takes time and is in ordered stages (66:7).

16

JEREMIAH

The earlier chapters of the book of Jeremiah are much concerned with lamenting the fact that the people of Israel have departed from the true faith and have turned to the worship of false gods. Jeremiah (thought to have been born about 650 BC, the son of the priest Hilkiah) likens Israel to a faithless wife who has left her husband and to a harlot whose lovers are really her enemies, out to destroy her. He specifically condemns the widespread worship of the queen of heaven, whom Ackerman[1] identifies as a syncretistic goddess who combines the characteristics of East Semitic Ishtar and West Semitic Astarte. Not only did the women of Jerusalem and Judah burn incense and pour libations to the goddess, but they baked cakes 'in her image' as sacrifical offerings (7:18, 44:19).

In contrast to Job's miseries, which were self-centred, Jeremiah's forebodings are about the purity of the nation's faith. Circumcision (4:4) is the outward sign of a true Israelite (see page 16) and requires men's minds (the ancients ascribed emotions to the heart) to be consumed with their faith. Unless Jeremiah is referring to the anguish of sin, verse 4:19 is a good description of angina pectoris or ischaemic heart disease. No one should miss reading 4:22: 'They are skilled in doing evil.'

NITROGEN CYCLE

Jeremiah indulges in local knowledge; Gilead (8:22) is close to his home town, Anathoth, which was noted for its styrax trees whose sap was used as balm. Physicians may comfort patients but health is secured by engineering works such as clean water supplies, disposal of excreta and waste, adequate food, control of pests and vectors, and good housing. Diseases are deadly because people die of them (16:4), but Jeremiah can be forgiven this tautology because he goes on to display, even unwittingly, knowledge of the nitrogen cycle. He is more explicit later (25:33) and repeats that corpses shall be as dung. Without entering into the rights and wrongs of organic farming, Western countries are profligate with nitrogen (excreta-provided) manure. The Chinese hyacinth pond is a near-perfect example of conservation. Excreta drop into a pond in which hyacinths are grown; the plants are raked off periodically, dried in the sun and fed to pigs. The water is kept free of mosquito larvae, *Culex* (see page 30), by Siamese fighting fish which can be caught and eaten.

ALARM AND DESPONDENCY

Looked at from the point of view of the civil authorities who were engaged in a war against Babylon, Jeremiah was spreading alarm and despondency. He was beaten and placed in the stocks (20:2). Though he was accused as a collaborator (27:17) he was judged by the princes, priests and prophets (26:16), who recognised his sincerity, as not deserving death. The civil authorities seem to have become tired of the lesser prophets who constantly prophesied woe to the state (29:26) and dealt with them by calling them mad, a foretaste of compulsory confinement (with painful treatments) of dissidents in what was the USSR. As the Gospels show, some lunatics were allowed to run wild, living as best they could. Others, no doubt, were subject to harsher treatment: not that the Western world can pride itself on kindly custodial care of the insane. The Israelites considered that insanity, like all illness, was the result of sin, but, because of the fear provoked by insanity, it was particularly heinous. Archaic memories explain why lunatics were so cruelly treated – being kept naked in chains, whipped and drenched with cold water – until 1705 when Pinel in Paris, followed by Tuke in York, made the experiment of the kindly custody of the insane.

GUILT

Textbooks of psychiatry are notably deficient about guilt (30:15); guilt is the reproach of conscience at the failure to conform to an accepted standard of behaviour either social or personal. This begs the question as to what is conscience. Very simplistically, Freud divided the mind into the unconscious (in the depths of which is the id, the driving force) and the conscious (which includes the ego seeking to satisfy the wishes of the id). The super-ego, partly in unconsciousness and partly in consciousness, acts as a censor, warning the ego when actions would not be acceptable. What is acceptable is determined almost entirely by cultural (including religious) effects on the human mind. That is why the family is so important. Anxiety arising from failure to meet standards prescribed either for the individual or by the individual for himself will cause much misery and terror of mind (30:5) (see page 246).

THE RECHABITES

Jeremiah was instrumental in saving the Rechabites, who, fleeing from the armies of Nebuchadnezzar, had recently arrived in Jerusalem, and who, by conviction did not drink wine, from the wrath of Jehoiakim, the king (35:1–19).

PRISON

Jeremiah was confined to the guardroom of the king's palace during the second siege of Jerusalem by Nebuchadnezzar (32:2). While he was there he prophesied that Zedekiah, the last king of Judah, would not die by the sword but in peace (34:5). It is the manner of death which is important and dying by the sword meant being hacked to death while fully conscious with a semi-blunt instrument.

Jeremiah was thrown into prison (37:15), as it was thought that he was trying to desert the Babylonians. In prison he announced that anyone who stayed in Jerusalem would perish by the sword but anyone who went over to the Babylonians would live. As a result of this ill-advised remark he was cast into a cistern (38:6) from which he was rescued by order of Zedekiah (38:10). He was returned to the guardroom of the palace, telling Zedekiah that he should surrender to the armies of Nebuchadnezzar (38:17–21). Zedekiah was a kindly but weak man who had not the courage to act in accordance with Jeremiah's advice. When Jerusalem finally fell to Nebuchadnezzar, Jeremiah was unharmed, but Zedekiah was captured as he fled. His two sons were slaughtered before him, and then his eyes were put out. Whether this was done by gouging them out or by the insertion of a hot poker, it must have been very gory and painful. After this Zedekiah was put in fetters for the journey to Babylon (39:7). With him went the élite of Judah forming the vanguard of the second exile in 587 BC (see page 155). Only the poorest of the land were left behind to struggle as best they could (40:7). Given the choice of whether to go to Babylon or not (40:6), Jeremiah chose to stay in Mizpah in Judah.

EGYPT

Nebuchadnezzar appointed Gedaliah, a friend of Jeremiah, governor over Judah (40:7) and he made his residence at

Mizpah. In some quarters Gedaliah was regarded as a collaborator, and Ishmael, a member of the royal house, hatched a plot to kill him. Gedaliah, together with a small Babylonian garrison and a number of innocent Israelites were killed (41:3, 7). Ishmael threw the corpses into the town's cistern, thus contaminating the water supply (41:9). Ishmael then escaped to the Ammonites, and the Israelites involved in the affair, fearing the vengeance of Nebuchadnezzar, fled to Egypt and took a reluctant Jeremiah with them (43:6).

When he was in Egypt, Jeremiah inveighed against those Israelites who apostasised and worshipped other gods (44:11 – 17). The final section of the book of Jeremiah consists of a series of prophecies against all the heathen nations, but especially against Babylon.

There is no record that Jeremiah ever left Egypt, though much legend surrounds his last years.

References

1. Ackerman S. 'And the Women Knead Dough' The Worship of the Queen of Heaven in Sixth-Century Judah : *Gender and Difference in Ancient Israel,* ed. Day P.L. Minneapolis: Fortress Press, 1989.

17

EZEKIEL

Ezekiel was the son of Buzi (1:3), who is known to have been a priest,[1] and very likely was well acquainted with Temple procedures from an early age. He was taken captive to Babylon by Nebuchadnezzar with the first group of exiles in 597 BC, ten years before the final destruction of Jerusalem.

Ezekiel was deeply affected by the sudden death of his wife, which took place shortly before Jerusalem fell: ' . . . and at evening my wife died' (24:18). She had been 'the delight of [his] eyes' (24:16). But life had to go on and despite his grief he did as the Lord commanded (24:18), continuing to warn about the fate of Israel and other nations. Death of a spouse, especially for men over the age of 55, is the most traumatic of life's events.[2] Mortality of widowers is 1.4 compared with 1 for married men (an increase of 40 per cent). However mediated, the commonest causes are coronary heart disease and other arterio-sclerotic diseases. There is a slight social gradient; presumably Ezekiel, being a priest, would be classified by the Registrar-General (see page 4) as Class I or II. He was lucky to survive his misery, especially as he was among the higher ranks of society.

Before the fall of Jerusalem, Ezekiel prophesied the downfall of the state and the captivity of the people, events brought about because Israel had been disobedient to the commands of the Lord. After the final fall of

Jerusalem in 587 BC and the second deportation, Ezekiel looked forward to the time when, as a result of her sufferings, Israel's heart would be changed (36:26), she would repent of her faithlessness and a holy people would be restored to a holy land. The fact that the exiles in Babylon preserved their national identity and faith owes much to the preaching and prophecy of Ezekiel. Undoubtedly he was a good man, if of extreme views, but then all prophets must be extreme. Incidents recorded by Ezekiel are of little medical interest, but his illusory percepts are.

EZEKIEL'S VISIONS

The opening chapters of the book are reminiscent of the hallucinations of GPI (general paralysis of the insane), from which Ezekiel could not have suffered as syphilis had not reached the Old World. Strong visual images (often with a sexual content) continue throughout the book. Chapters 16 and 23 must have been well read in boys' schools, as least before the days of the permissive society. The lewd goings-on of two sisters, Oholah and Oholibah, who prostituted themselves with all who came, including the Babylonians, and who are killed for their misdeeds, are an allegory explaining the fate of Samaria and Jerusalem, who have committed adultery by worshipping idols, defiling the Lord's sanctuary and profaning the Sabbath (23:1ff.).

Ezekiel was an unusual child if his play did not include imitating his father at his Temple duties. No doubt he also mimicked his father's exhortations. 'A large part of the thinking of children consists of visual images, some children being capable of visual images of such vividness and detail that, as an experience, it is virtually identical with, and may be mistaken for, visual perceiving; imagery of this clarity and intensity is called "eidetic". Visual imagery tends to decline in importance as children grow older ... A few adults retain a capacity for "eidetic" imagery.'[3]

Ezekiel's thought processes retained eidetic processes. The strong sexual overlay and fixed inadaptable goals are thus explained. No wonder he made a good watchman (3:17, 33:7).

EZEKIEL'S TEMPLE

In the later chapters, Ezekiel's fear that the commerce and luxury of Babylon might pervert the faith of the exiles is the more understandable if it is remembered that he was taken to Babylon as a captive. The last chapters (40:1ff.) describe how, in a dream, he was shown the architectural details of the restored Temple complex of the new Jerusalem which symbolises Yahweh in the midst of his redeemed people. In his description (see page 58) Ezekiel is influenced primarily by his memories of the Temple of Solomon, but also by the fortified sanctuaries of Babylonia and his own distinctive theological viewpoint.

References

1. Muilenburg J. Ezekiel: *Peake's Commentary on the Bible.* London: Nelson, 1962.
2. Parkes C.M., Benjamin B., Fitzgerald R.G. Broken Heart: A Statistical Study of Increased Mortality among Widowers. *British Medical Journal.* 1969, i: 740.
3. Russell Davies D. *Introduction to Psychopathology.* Oxford: Oxford University Press, 1957.

18

DANIEL

Most, if not all, of the book of Daniel was written during the rule of Antiochus Epiphanes (175–163 BC) to give guidance to loyal Jews faced with the problems of living under a pagan dictatorship. It is not based on history or fact. The author(s) had sufficient insight to keep the dreams of Nebuchadnezzar and Daniel (ignoring Belshazzar's indigestion) within the bounds of reality and thus comment on the medical aspects of the stories is justified.

VEGETARIANISM

Daniel and his friends Shadrach, Meshach and Abednego were among the élite of Judah who were taken captive to Babylon by Nebuchadnezzar. Because of their intelligence and good looks they were to be educated in the king's palace for three years and at the end of that time they would be members of the king's staff (1:4–6). They were given a daily portion of the rich food which the king ate and of the wine which he drank. To escape eating the king's food and drinking his wine the four youths managed to organise a clinical trial – perhaps the first on record – for themselves on a vegetarian diet for ten days (1:12). At the end of that time they were better in appearance and fatter than those youths who had eaten the king's food (1:15). For a nutritional trial it was far too short.

NEBUCHADNEZZAR'S DREAM

Nebuchadnezzar woke up from a nightmare (2:1): he could not remember it, but demanded an explanation of it. The court magicians were threatened with death for their inability to interpret the dream (but were later saved by Daniel). Daniel was cleverer than the court magicians; he made up a dream, interpreting it to satisfy Nebuchadnezzar's regal pretensions. Later, Daniel interpreted another of Nebuchadnezzar's dreams (4:10–18), entreating him to practise righteousness and show mercy so that there might be a lengthening of his tranquillity (4:27). This shows some bravery on the part of Daniel. A year after this, Nebuchadnezzar behaved very eccentrically, eating grass and not trimming his hair and nails (4:33).

THE FIERY FURNACE

In spite of the difficulty the Israelites had in achieving a temperature higher than 400°C by burning wood (see page 57), the furnace prepared for Shadrach, Meshach and Abednego was seven times hotter than normal (3:19). The Song of the Three Young Men in the Apocrypha says that the fire consisted of naphtha, pitch, tar and brushwood. Naphtha is a fraction of petroleum which presumably oozed from exposed horizontal strata of the earth. Pitch is present as deposits of bitumen on the floor of the Dead Sea. Naphtha has a low flashpoint but, like pitch, would not have increased the temperature of burning wood. No one can be expected to take this story literally. The survival of Shadrach, Meshach and Abednego is an oblique (or not so oblique) allusion to the emergence of Israel from tribulation.

BELSHAZZAR'S FEAST

Belshazzar, who had succeeded his father Nebuchadnezzar, gave a banquet (5:1). The guests, including the king, were drunk, and in his inebriation Belshazzar magnified the shadows on the wall to fingers which wrote (5:5). Belshazzar suffered acute indigestion from an over full stomach which embarrassed the action of his heart (5:6). Earlier generations of physicians distinguished between indigestion and malignant indigestion from which the patient might die. The diagnosis of acute pain in the epigastrium or behind the sternum can be difficult. Clearly, acute coronary insufficiency is a major cause. Though electrocardiography was introduced in 1910 by Einthoven, it did not fulfil its potential in distinguishing coronary insufficiency from other causes of substernal pain until the late 1920s when portable apparatus with immediate recording on paper was developed. Daniel, in spite of his unfavourable interpretation of the writing on the wall, which he said involved the break-up of the kingdom, was clothed in purple and made the third ruler in the kingdom. That same night Belshazzar was slain and the kingdom came under the control of Darius, a Persian ruler (5:30).

DANIEL IN THE LION'S DEN

Darius was so pleased with Daniel that he made him one of three presidents over 120 satraps. The other administrators were jealous of Daniel and proposed a decree which they knew he would not obey. As a result Daniel was cast into the lions' den (6:16). The lions did not attack Daniel; perhaps they were well fed or perhaps they left hunting and killing to lionesses as they do in the wild, but Daniel may not have known this. During the night in which Daniel was in the lions' den, Darius fasted and no diversions were brought to him (6:18). This probably means that he had no young girls in his bed. Daniel was released the next morning at the command of Darius (6:23).

DANIEL'S DREAMS

Daniel recounts his own dreams (7:1), which seem to have upset him as he changed colour as Belshazzar did. Stimulation of the sympathetic nerves or inhibition of the vagal system would account for this: ' . . . my spirit within me was anxious and the visions of my head alarmed me' (7:15), which is not surprising as Daniel in his career underwent rapid change from honour to infamy. He did not understand his anxiety neurosis (8:27), for, had he done so, he would not have had one. A night in the lions' den at the order of Darius, whose high favour he had recently received, was close to the psychologically insupportable. Afterwards he did not receive any psychological help except in a dream from the angel Gabriel, who was wholly ineffective (8:17). Daniel was a man of strong character, who, unlike Pavlov's dogs (see page 247), responded neither by excitement nor by inhibition but continued to hold his God in awe (9:4) and was greatly distressed by the evil around him. Daniel's last dream (10:4) was caused by exhaustion consequent on fasting.

19

THE MINOR PROPHETS

Of the minor prophets, Hosea, Joel, Amos, Obadiah, Jonah, Micah, Nahum, Habakkuk, Zephaniah, Haggai, Zechariah and Malachi, only Zechariah and Malachi record incidents of medical interest.

ZECHARIAH

Zechariah sees Wickedness as a woman sitting in an ephah (a large jar) (5:8). He watched as an angel thrust the woman back into the jar and weighted the lid with lead.

Zechariah visualises the restoration of Jerusalem. A dire plague is promised for those who wage war against her (14:12). Besides man, horses, mules, camels and asses together with other beasts will be affected. The symptoms will be rotting of the flesh while still on one's feet, rotting of eyes while still in their sockets and rotting of tongues while still in the mouth. If the symptoms are to be taken as applying to a clinical syndrome, it is chronic rather than acute, but after that, the whole gamut of infectious disease can be run through. The mention of horses suggests glanders (facy), a disease due to infection with *Bacillus mallei* in which indurated ulcers affect the tongue. Similar lesions of the oropharynx and trachea (windpipe) seriously reduce ability to breathe. Glanders is of low infectivity but may occasionally affect men in close contact with horses.

185

Though the infectivity of foot-and-mouth disease between cloven-hoofed animals (which include the animals listed) is very high, the infectivity to man is low. The virus of foot-and-mouth disease is among the smallest but it is extremely persistent. In man, foot-and-mouth disease is characterised by fever, salivation, vesicles affecting the mouth and pharynx, and vesicles on the skin of the palms, fingers, feet and toes.

Pain around the eyeballs is frequent in trichiniasis (see page 62) owing to the extrinsic muscles of the eye being affected. Malta fever (brucellosis) spread by milk infected with *Bacillus abortus of Bang* is, in unsanitised countries, a possible cause of wasting affecting both man and animals. In animals abortion is common.

Tuberculosis (wasting disease) was rife even in the absence of threats by Zechariah. Very probably all the diseases mentioned existed concurrently, but, if one has to be chosen, foot-and-mouth disease is preferred.

MALACHI

Malachi (3:2) talks about fullers' soap. As explained on page 95, the Hebrews did not have saponified soap. Malachi uses the Hebrew *bōrîth*, which means alkali or potash and is derived from *bōr*, which means lye or potash used in smelting. The word for fullers is *khobᵉsîm*, which is derived from the verb *kābhas*, to clean cloth by treading, kneading and beating, thus to wash. Fullers must have suffered from dermatitis.

20

THE APOCRYPHA

BACKGROUND NOTE

After the completion of the Temple in 515 BC, Palestine continued under the domination of the Persian empire until Persia was defeated by Alexander the Great. Following the death of Alexander in 323 BC his empire was divided among his generals. Ptolemy controlled Egypt while Seleucus was paramount in Asia. Both dynasties coveted Palestine, which eventually fell to Ptolemy. The Ptolemies ruled Palestine until 199 BC, when Antiochus III, a Seleucid king, took advantage of the political weakness of the Ptolemies and annexed Palestine. Antiochus III was succeeded by Seleucus IV (187–175 BC), who was followed by Antiochus IV, Epiphanes, (175–163 BC). For the Jews the advent of the Seleucids meant oppression, which came to a peak during the reign of Antiochus Epiphanes.

As a result of Alexander the Great's conquests, Greek civilisation advanced throughout the whole of the Eastern Mediterranean and much of South-Western Asia. Greek became the language of government, commerce and religion, and with language went the habits and culture of Greece. Alexander was a Macedonian and his army was mainly recruited from Macedon and the city states of Greece. During his advances and retreats Alexander used to leave groups of soldiers, who, with his encouragement, had married local girls and had become too old to fight, to form settlements (see page 51). This encouraged the process of Hellenisation which affected Judaea in common with her neighbours. By the time the Seleucids annexed Palestine, there was already a strong Hellenistic party in Jerusalem, led by Jason, the brother of Onias III, the High Priest.

The books of the Apocrypha were written in, or relate to, the period of Seleucid and Ptolemaic rule in Egypt and Palestine. None of the books of the Apocrypha is included in the Hebrew canon of Scripture. All of them, however, with the exception of II Esdras, are present in the Greek version of the Old Testament known as the Septuagint (see page 48).

I ESDRAS

I Esdras does not invite medical comment. It reproduces the substance of Chronicles, the whole of Ezra and some of Nehemiah. There are numerous minor discrepancies between the apocryphal and the canonical accounts. In particular, the story of the three young men at the court of King Darius (3:4ff.) has no parallel in the Old Testament. The king decided that Zerubbabel was the wisest of his three young bodyguards because he argued that women were stronger than men or wine but that truth is the strongest of all things. According to the story, Darius rewarded Zerubbabel by agreeing to the rebuilding of the Temple in Jerusalem and the return of the treasure looted by Nebuchadnezzar.

II ESDRAS

II Esdras in important theologically in that the author, Esdras, argues at great length with the archangel Uriel, representing the Lord, about the problem of theodicy. The author's mood cannot be called anything but depressed and his constant anxiety is that many, if not most, of the Jews have failed to observe the law. Personal responsibility for one's mode of life is emphasised (7:59). The author is sure that the law will never perish (9:37) but compliance with the law is, of itself, inadequate for salvation, for there is no man who has not sinned. All have need of the divine mercy (8:32). In this, the book presages the teaching of St Paul (Galatians 2:16).

Much of the book consists of reports of dreams, e.g. the woman without grandchildren (9:38), the eagle with twelve feathered wings and three heads (11:1) and the lion with a man's voice (11:37). In terms of Jung's psychoanalysis the author's personal consciousness is strongly implanted with the collective unconscious. The writing shows a high degree of intuition and the author fails to realise that his perceptions were mediated by his own conscious mind.

The sweeping statement that an older woman bears smaller children (5:51) is not entirely borne out by figures collated in recent years in Britain. The median birth weight of babies tends to increase with parity though in later pregnancies the incidence of unexplained low birth weight and of illness is increased slightly. The incidence of medical and mental abnormality in the baby is increased for older mothers. What is true in Britain today may not have been for Israelite women living in different social conditions where food was often sparse and very likely they ate last. An ill-nourished mother would be unable to nourish her foetus and low birth weight may well have been the norm.

TOBIT

Tobit's principal value lies in the picture it gives of Jewish culture in the second century BC. It is a boy meets girl story. Tobit, a righteous Jewish refugee living in Nineveh, realised that he had been wrong in doubting his wife's honesty and that his subsequent reproaches to her were unjustified. After moaning to the Lord, he became blind, which was ascribed to the fact that sparrow droppings had fallen on his eyelids (2:10) but in fact was conversion hysteria.

Tobit remembered that twenty years previously he had deposited some money with Gabael, who lived at Rages. Tobit sent his son Tobias to fetch the money. Tobias, accompanied by his dog, was guided by Azarias, in reality the angel Raphael disguised as a man. On the way to Rages, Tobias and Azarias stayed with Raguel, at Ecbatana. Raguel had a daughter, Sarah, who had had seven husbands who had all died entering the honeymoon suite, apparently without raising any suspicion (except in the minds of the maids whom Sarah had beaten). Azarias told Tobias that he would marry Sarah and overcome the demon who had killed her previous seven husbands. Raguel seems to have been glad to have 'given' Sarah to Tobias, and it must be admitted that the marriage seems to have been successful, if only because they had a number of children. When Tobias returned home with his bride, his dog and the money which Azarias had collected for him from Gabael, Tobit's vision recovered. This is the only time in the Bible or the Apocrypha in which a dog is portrayed as a faithful companion.

JUDITH

The story is of how Holofernes's lust for Judith betrayed his duty, which, as one of Nebuchadnezzar's generals, was to ravage Bethulia and plunder the remainder of Israel. While Holofernes was somnolent after drinking wine with her, Judith is said to have cut off his head with two blows from his sword (13:8). The Greek *akinakēs* means a short straight Persian sword. In time and with much bloody mess she may have decapitated him, but not with the ease or swiftness described (see page 125).

ECCLESIASTICUS

Homilies might well be written, with profit to both the priest and the congregation, on all the precepts in Ecclesiasticus, which is a book of profound wisdom mixed with common sense. This would be a welcome change to many a dull sermon. Not many of the precepts call for medical comment. Wisdom comes from the Lord (1:1) and was created before all things (1:4). Because the Greek *sophia* is a feminine noun, wisdom is thereafter referred to as feminine. Wisdom is identified with the law (1:26, 19:20), a concept which is found here for the first time in Jewish literature. 'Happy is the husband of a good wife . . .' (26:1) but in spite of this the gender tone (presumably reflecting the mores of the time) is that women are subordinate, something a man has around the house: 'He who acquires a wife gets his best possession' (36:24).

The advice to him who loves a son to whip him often (30:1ff.) reflects Proverbs 13:24: 'He who spares the rod hates his son, but he who loves him is diligent to discipline him.' This is exactly the wrong way to bring up children, conditioning them to pain and cruelty and possibly giving rise to sado-masochism. Anxieties about daughters are those of a permissive society (42:9), but most probably girls had little choice in what they did. The shame of unmarried pregnancy is stressed (42:10). Women were expected to live in their father's or husband's house.

There are frequent instructions on how to keep healthy – for example, avoid unjustified anger (1:22), early to bed and early to rise, eat moderately (31:20), avoid excess alcohol (31:29) and think sensibly about death (41:1ff.). Old men are enjoined to remember that they were once young (42:8), and ideas should not be overlooked (32:18). Without being too far-fetched it is possible to suppose that Freud's theories about dreams (including the sexual drive) were anticipated (34:1ff.). When everything is ascribed to the Lord, as it is throughout the Bible, enquiries into the workings of the mind are stifled. As has been said earlier, the Hebrews had little psychiatric understanding. There is a tribute to the work of the physician (38:1–8), but the skill of the physician is derived from God.

The statement 'Every creature loves its like . . . and a man clings to one like himself' (13:15) is highly significant in relation both to the formation of a culture and to tortures which are endured in Maccabees (see page 194).

I AND II MACCABEES

I Maccabees gives a detailed account of the Jewish struggle for religious liberty and political independence from the accession of Antiochus Epiphanes in 175 BC to the death of Simon Maccabeus in 135 BC. The main part of this narrative is elaborated by II Maccabees, which, though not so trustworthy historically, is a fascinating story of perfidy, murder and the vilest torture.

During the reign of Seleucus IV (187–175 BC), Heliodorus was ordered to plunder the Temple in Jerusalem. When he tried to enter the Temple treasury he fainted from terror (II.3:24ff.). There is a vague suggestion that this may have caused hysterical overbreathing with consequent tetany (contraction of the muscles first seen in the hands and feet). He recovered when Onias III, the High Priest, offered the sacrifice of atonement (II.3:32).

Seleucus IV was succeeded by Antiochus Epiphanes (175–163 BC). Onias was away and Jason offered the new king 440 talents of silver for the office of High Priest and promised to support his Hellenisation policy, including the building of a gymnasium for the Jewish youth (I.1:11–15, II.4:7–17). In the gymnasium the Greek games in the nude would take place (against the Jewish canon). Complete nudity has little sexual focus and it is a matter of taste whether it is better than the skimpy clothes of modern athletes. The more women are uncovered the better they are treated; a point proved by the Islamic chador.

Three years later Menelaus offered Antiochus even more money for the office of High Priest; Jason was promptly deposed and Menelaus installed in his place (II.4:24). He was even more unscrupulous than his predecessor and, when he could not raise the bribe he had promised the king, he stole the golden vessels from the Temple (II.4:32). Onias was treacherously murdered when he exposed these thefts (II.4:34), but his murderer, Andronicus, met with a punishment that fitted the crime (II.4:38). Of note is the apt phrase 'advanced in years and no less advanced in folly' (II.4:40).

After a false report of Antiochus's death, Jason, hoping to recover the office of High Priest, attacked Jerusalem with a force of one thousand men. He did not realise that success at the cost of killing one's kindred is 'the greatest misfortune' (II.5:6). Eventually, 8000 persons including women, virgins and infants, were killed and many sold into slavery.

In 167 BC Antiochus decided, with the help of Menelaus, to enforce Hellenisation on the reluctant Jews. He issued a proclamation forbidding the people to live any longer according to the law of Moses. The aim was the complete abolition of the Jewish religion. Regular sacrifices were suspended, Sabbath observance was forbidden, circumcision was abolished and copies of the law were to be destroyed. Pagan altars were set up throughout the land, Jews were forced to sacrifice at these and eat swine's flesh, and the worship of Zeus was introduced into the Temple in Jerusalem. Soon all Judaea was in revolt and those who refused to comply with Antiochus's decrees were punished severely.

An aged and much respected scribe, Eleazar, was cruelly killed for refusing to 'eat swine's flesh' (II.6:18 – 31). Some of his torturers offered to substitute permitted food for the swine flesh, but he preferred further torture and death because of the example it would set. A mother was made to watch her seven sons tortured in order of seniority by having their tongues cut out, being scalped and their hands and feet chopped off before they were fried in oil. She was then treated in the same way herself (II.7:1ff.). The second son is reported as speaking soon after having his tongue cut out – a most remarkable feat (II.7:9). If these stories are true, all one can hope is that the loss of blood reduced consciousness to a minimum before the victims were thrown into the hot oil.

The mind of Antiochus, who gave the orders and watched the proceedings, must have been pathologically deranged. Sadism breeds sadism. In ethically controversial experiments[1] to determine why orders of this sort are obeyed, actors took the part of 'students' and were punished for making alleged mistakes by simulated electric shocks, supposedly graded from mild to severe pain. A high proportion of 'teachers' (those administering the punishment, often under protest) increased the shock to the point of causing 'agony'. Decent men surrender their consciences to organised authority, whether democratic or dictatorial in origin, which expects to be obeyed and which they expect to obey. Their personality is merged in the organisational structure with its inequalities of human relationship. Defiance of orders involves loss of peer 'sameness'.

Widespread individual acts of defiance turned into a general rebellion when Mattathias, a priest, refused to sacrifice on the pagan altar. Seeing a Jew about to offer the sacrifice, he killed him. He also killed the king's enforcing officer. Then with his five sons, Mattathias fled to the hills, calling on all who were zealous for the law to follow him (I.2:15–27). Thus began the Maccabean revolt. The five sons, Judas, John, Simon, Eleazar and Jonathan, carried on the struggle after the death of their father.

When Antiochus was absent in Ecbatana, he had an attack of colic while driving in his chariot, which caused him to fall out, sustaining multiple injuries (II.9:5). The suddenness of onset suggests enteritis due to the ingestion in food of an exo-toxin (heat stable) secreted by some types of *Staphylococcus* allowed to incubate in food. The onset of symptoms is very sudden and accompanied by extreme prostration which not infrequently proceeds to a fatal outcome. So far as staphylococcal organisms are concerned, these are present on the skin and often in the nose. Picking the nose while handling food is highly dangerous and, of course, hands must be thoroughly washed with soap under running water, which in Britain, ideally, means a mixer with the taps controlled by long elbow arms.

Antiochus appears to have recovered from his diarrhoea, but then his wounds produced such a smell that no one would go near him (II.9:10). Almost certainly he developed gas gangrene due to infection of his wounds with *Clostridia perfrigens (bacillus welchii)*. *C. perfrigens* is present in human and animal faeces. As *C. perfrigens* is spore forming this makes churned-up ground especially dangerous, as in the First World War. *C. perfrigens* grows anaerobically and in deep wounds causes necrosis of tissue and haemolysis. Gas is produced, at first odourless carbon dioxide and hydrogen, later hydrogen sulphide and indols are present, causing a most offensive smell. Without treatment by antitoxin and/or antibiotics, prognosis is uniformly fatal.

If Antiochus was carrying *C. perfrigens* in his bowel, his profuse diarrhoea may have infected his wounds in addition to the risk from the dung of the horses used to draw his chariot. Later, his body swarmed with 'worms' (II.9:9).

In tropical climates flies may lay eggs in wounds, especially as they are often dirty, and if Antiochus's wounds were contaminated with faeces this would have been an ideal breeding ground. Eggs are laid and these mature to maggots. Usually, apart from the appearance, these are innocuous, but some maggots (e.g. of the botfly, one host of which is the horse) may destroy the wound tissue. *Nematodes*, such as the round worm (see page 63), present in faeces have to be distinguished from maggots. Antiochus was vilely cruel, but to write a letter before his death advocating a policy of moderation to his successors took courage (II.9:19–27).

Judas Maccabeus made good use of the absence of Antiochus and in 164 BC he captured Jerusalem and cleansed and rededicated the Temple (I.4:36, II.10:1ff.). The original object of the revolt had been achieved: the Jews had gained religious freedom.

Before his death Antiochus had appointed Lysias as regent for his son, Antiochus V, Eupator, who was only 9 years old. Judas Maccabeus, not content with obtaining religious freedom, now sought political freedom. This caused Lysias to attack Judaea. There were many minor wars, and for a time relations between Lysias and Judas improved to the extent that letters were sent to Jews in the Diaspora telling them that they might return with safety (II.11:27). Many governors did not accept the improved relations between Maccabeus and Lysias. There were minor skirmishes, in one of which Dositheus, a Greek, had his arm cut off while trying to capture Gorgias (II.12:35). Judas took a collection from his men of the plunder from the dead and wounded Greeks and sent it to Jerusalem to provide for a sin offering (II.12:43).

Intrigue among the Greeks resulted in Menelaus being taken to Aleppo and put to death by being dropped into hot ashes from a tower 50 cubits – about 92 feet (28 m) – high (II.13:5).

Lysias again attacked Judas Maccabeus, and in a fierce battle Eleazar, the brother of Judas, stabbed the elephant which he thought was carrying the young king, Antiochus V, and was crushed to death by the beast as it fell (I.6:46, II.13:15). Lysias had to withdraw to deal with trouble in Syria, but before doing so he made peace with Judas

Maccabeus, granting the Jews complete religious freedom and recognising Judas as the king's representative in Judaea (II.13:23).

III MACCABEES

The atrocities committed by Ptolemy IV, Philopater, against the Jews in Egypt provide the background to III Maccabees. The Ptolemies saw themselves as successors to the Pharaohs and ruled as despots. Ptolemy IV (221 – 203 BC) is described by Justinus[2] in the sentence: '*Noctes in stupris, dies in conviviis consumit*' (he spends the nights in debauchery, the days in feasting). He was a cyclothymic personality undergoing sudden and violent changes of mood.

At that time, Palestine was under the control of Egypt and with much publicity Ptolemy attempted to enter the holy of holies in the Temple in Jerusalem (1:10). He failed partly because of the bravery of the priests but more importantly because he was afraid of the uproar he had created among the populace. Simon, the High Priest, addressed the Lord, begging for his help (2:1ff.). Ptolemy then started shaking all over and became paralysed in his limbs. A modern physician called to such an incident would be asking himself whether Ptolemy had suffered a cerebro-vascular accident, such as thrombosis, embolism or even haemorrhage or whether he had a space occupying lesion such as a tumour in the brain. Cerebral malaria or lead encephalopathy (from white lead carbonate used in cosmetics) are outside possibilities. Ptolemy seems to have recovered fairly quickly and the diagnosis of hysteria (see page 246) must be raised. More likely Ptolemy was a malingerer using feigned (and, to his entourage, alarming) signs to save an arrogant (1:26) personality losing his regal 'face.'

Having returned to Egypt, Ptolemy determined to wreak vengeance on the Jews for his humiliation in Jerusalem. He issued a decree reducing them to the status of slaves and subjecting them to registration and poll tax if they did not accept the pagan cult of Dionysus (2:28). Most of the Jews refused to register or abandon their faith, and Ptolemy ordered cruel and unusual punishments including the threat of being trampled on by drunken elephants (5:1ff.).

The court officials fawned on Ptolemy and did not complain until they were forced to wonder about his mental instability (5:39) and they themselves were inconvenienced. Later, as a result of divine intervention, Ptolemy made reparation to the Jews. With his permission the Jews killed 300 men who had failed to keep their faith during the time of persecution (7:15). The story is one of a cruel and vicious dictator whose actions, even if not approved, were connived at by the non-Jewish populace, who were quite prepared to enjoy the spectacle of brutality.

IV MACCABEES

The author philosophises that rational judgement is the highest virtue (1:2), being able to rule the emotions, even those which hinder self-control. He goes on to discuss gluttony, lust, malice, pain, pleasure and other emotions. He assumes that rational judgement shows a life of wisdom (1:15). He comes close to equating beauty with sexual desire (2:1) and argues that rational judgement (2:17) controlled the anger of Moses (Leviticus 19:9) and King David's thirst after overcoming the Philistines (II Samuel 23:13). Much of his argument revolves around the torture of Eleazar, the seven brothers and their mother (see page 193). Later, he repeats with apparent gusto and no justification the nauseating details of their sufferings and endurance. Nowhere does he display, even to the slightest degree, any idea that refusal to eat pig, even under torture, was culturally induced. The law which prohibited this was of divine origin and, whatever the consequences, had to be obeyed. The Jews distinguished themselves and were distinguished by this obedience. Claims of sacrificial atonement are made (17:21), best expressed in

Eleazar's cry: 'Make my blood their purification, and take my life in exchange for theirs' (6:29).

References

1. Milgram S. *Obedience to Authority.* London: Tavistock Publications, Methuen, 1974.
2. Justinus. *Epitome Historiarum Philippicarum,* xxx. 1.8. : The Apocrypha and Pseudepigrapha of the Old Testament, ed. Charles R.H. Oxford: Clarendon Press, 1913.

21

THE GOSPELS

The Gospel according to Mark, the earliest Gospel, was probably written in Rome, about AD 65–70 and was based on the recollections of Peter. The language of Mark is simple and his account is generally accepted as the least blemished. Matthew and Luke both use Mark and add material from other sources. John, writing between AD 90–100, builds theological interpretation into the story. All the Gospels were written in *koinē* Greek, the common form of Greek, simplified from the classical standards, which had become widely used throughout the Middle East as a result of the campaigns of Alexander the Great.

BIRTH OF JESUS

Only Luke (1:27) and Matthew (1:23) develop the theme that Jesus was born of a virgin, Luke at length and Matthew briefly. In English the word 'virgin' has sexual and emotional overtones; the Greek *parthenos* may mean no more than an unmarried girl. Matthew believed Mary was a virgin in fulfilment of the prophecy of Isaiah (7:14), but Isaiah used the Hebrew *'alemāh*, which means a young woman, nubile or newly married. Probably the meaning is best conveyed by the idea of a nubile girl not yet having borne a child. This, of course, does not imply the absence of sexual intercourse.

200

Mary was visited by the angel Gabriel, who told her: 'you will conceive in your womb and bear a son' (Luke 1:31). He added 'The Holy Spirit will come upon you, and the power of the Most High will overshadow you' (Luke 1:35). This can mean quite simply that Mary is promised the birth of a child. It was a general Jewish belief that the birth of a child required three partners, a man, a woman and the Spirit of God. Without the presence of the Spirit the woman would remain barren.[1] Mary's reply was: 'I am the handmaid of the Lord; let it be to me according to your word' (Luke 1:38). Mary went in 'haste' to visit Elizabeth, a kinswoman, probably a description applied to a member of the same clan. Elizabeth was unexpectedly pregnant in view of her age and that of her husband, Zechariah (neither age is stated). When Mary arrived, Elizabeth was about six months pregnant (Luke 1:36) and regarded her pregnancy as due to the Lord's intervention (Luke 1:24). The first person to tell Zechariah of his wife's forthcoming pregnancy was the angel Gabriel. Zechariah was struck dumb, an hysterical aphonia, which had the advantage of avoiding confrontation with Elizabeth. Zechariah remained dumb until his son (who grew up to be John the Baptist) was circumcised eight days after his birth (Luke 1:59, 64). Shortly before John was born, Mary returned home. Joseph, to whom she was betrothed, was much upset when he discovered that she was pregnant but was assured when, in a dream, an angel of the Lord told him that she had conceived of the Holy Spirit (Matthew 1:20).

The second century apocryphal Book of James[2] is not included in the canon of the New Testament but it illuminates the problem of Jesus's conception over which the Gospels are reticent. According to the Book of James, Mary was the daughter of Ioacim, a rich shepherd, and his wife Anna. Ioacim was prevented from offering a gift to the Lord because he had no children. He retreated into the wilderness for forty days, during which time Anna lamented her 'widowhood' and childlessness. On the advice of Judith, her maid, Anna humbled herself before the Lord. Ioacim returned home, conception occurred: an example of the returning warrior syndrome and psychic calm in the woman (see page 119).

The chronology of events seems to be:

Birth. Mary, daughter of Ioacim and Anna – very pious parental ambitions developed in thanks for having a child.

Age 1 year. Blessed by priests who asked God to give her a name 'renowned forever among all generations'.

Age 2 years. Tentative move (foiled by Anna) to give Mary to the Temple priests.

Age 3 years. Given to the priests to be brought up in the Temple according to the promise made by Anna when she was lamenting her childlessness. The priest who received Mary said: 'The Lord hath magnified thy name among all generations.'

Age 12 years. 'Widowers of the people' summoned; Joseph selected and Mary given to him 'lest she pollute the sanctuary of the Lord'. Joseph protested: 'I am an old man but she is a girl: lest I become a laughing stock.' Joseph was persuaded to take Mary to his house and said to her: 'Now I do leave thee in my house, and I go away to build my buildings and I will come again unto thee.' A pattern of frequent (and possibly long) absences by Joseph seems to have been established.

Age 16 years. The priests wanted a veil for the Temple and collected seven pure virgins, among whom Mary was included, to make it. As she was starting to weave the purple and scarlet cloth Mary heard a voice: 'Hail, thou art highly favoured . . .' She perceived an angel (Gabriel) of the Lord who said: 'Thou shalt conceive of his word' and Mary was glad she would bring forth in the manner of women. Mary went to stay with Elizabeth, whose greeting was: 'Whence is this to me that the mother of my Lord should come unto me?' When Mary left Elizabeth after three months to return to her (and Joseph's) home she was three months pregnant. She hid herself in shame. Joseph returned from his building work when she was six months pregnant. He was deeply shocked and worried lest people thought he had had intercourse with her. His anxieties were relieved in a dream in which an angel appeared and told him that Mary's child was of the Holy Ghost. An enquiry by the priests accepted Mary's statement: 'As the Lord my God liveth, I am pure before him and I know not a man' and absolved her and Joseph from any wrongdoing.

Age 16½ years. In Bethlehem, where Mary and Joseph had gone to register under the decree of Caesar Augustus, Joseph wondered whether to register Mary as his wife. It is interesting that Luke (2:5) even at this point in time refers to Mary as Joseph's betrothed, not his wife. An example of Joseph's consideration for her is that during the journey he sat Mary on his ass instead of letting her walk carrying all the luggage as other women would whether they were pregnant or not. Joseph and his son walked. Mary went into labour and Joseph met a midwife. Jesus was born. The midwife believed in the virgin birth, but Salome, a friend of the midwife, did not until after further questioning of Mary.

Seven facts are evident.

1. Under stress Zechariah developed an hysterical loss of voice.
2. Gabriel was a man (see page 16).
3. Neither in the Gospels nor in the Book of James is there any suggestion that Joseph impregnated Mary, though later the Jews, accusing Jesus of being illegitimate, referred to him as the supposed son of Joseph (see page 205).
4. Both Zechariah and Gabriel had access to Elizabeth and Mary. In an elegant paper Bostock[1] suggests that Zechariah was the father of Jesus. It is not unknown for modern husbands to dally with the *au pair* girl, but it seems highly improbable that Zechariah would, in view of his age, do this with Mary to the point of having penetrative intercourse. Zechariah himself, when told by Gabriel of

Elizabeth's forthcoming pregnancy, asked how that could be because he was an old man (though this is not conclusive evidence of non-paternity). He added that Elizabeth was of advanced years. Gabriel had pre-knowledge of Elizabeth's pregnancy and of Mary's pregnancy, or the likelihood of it. On the grounds of probability, Gabriel was the impregnator of both Elizabeth and Mary.

5.   Mary had been strongly imprinted, almost since birth, with the idea that she had a special duty to the Lord. During her upbringing in the Temple, the priests are likely to have enhanced this. Indeed, her reply to Gabriel: 'I am the handmaid of the Lord; let it be to me according to your word' (Luke 1:38), suggests that she was preconditioned to accepting any suggestion that Gabriel, as a messenger from the Lord, might have made to her.

6.   Any duty she may have had to Joseph was far outweighed by her duty to the Lord; because of this she did not think that she had committed a moral offence.

7.   Mary's suggestibility was, as it often is, associated with ability to dissociate. Hysterical amnesia obliterated the memory of her intercourse with Gabriel.

THE JOSEPH – MARY FAMILY

Whatever else he was, Jesus was human, a man who in the course of his life was able to withstand physical hardship, mental stress and moral temptation. His genome must have included an X chromosome (supplied by Mary) and a Y chromosome. Who supplied the Y chromosome is of no medical significance. After Jesus left the Decapolis and Galilee (Mark 5:21) and reached the neighbourhood of Bethlehem (Mark 6:3), the crowd, presumably made up of local people who knew him, referred to him as: 'the son of Mary and brother of James and Joses and Judas and Simon'. The epithet 'son of Mary' could be a deliberate slight: customarily Jesus would have been known as 'bar Joseph', even after Joseph's death. Luke raises similar doubts: 'Jesus . . . being the son (as was supposed) of Joseph' (Luke 3:23) but later, when Jesus was speaking to the crowd, the people asked: 'Is not this Joseph's son?' (Luke 4:22). Clearly some doubt as to Jesus's legitimacy or illegitimacy was abroad, if only to be raised on hostile occasions. The Jews were, to use modern parlance, slapped down when they provoked Jesus by saying: 'We were not born of fornication; we have one Father, even God' (John 8:41).

There remains one paramount matter. The Joseph – Mary family must have been outstanding, exceeding previous and subsequent families in love and care. Joseph's treatment of his fiancée, pregnant in circumstances which caused him much distress, is proof of his tenderness, exemplified in the ride to Bethlehem. Marians might well reflect on this. Joseph gave unstinted fatherly affection; whether he was Jesus's biological father does not matter, he filled the role of a father to the full. Mary's personal traits would not alter, but there are no further reports (among the little that is said) that suggests hysterical (dissociated) incidents. Her suggestibility may have been linked with sensitivity to other people. She had been well schooled in Hebrew history and law by the priests and very likely Jesus's knowledge was derived from her. In the family it is the mother, more than anyone else, who sets the psychological and social ambience, of gentleness, consideration and care. Joseph is thought to have died before Jesus started his ministry. The final and the lasting word is that of John (1:14): 'And the Word became flesh and dwelt among us, full of grace and truth.'

BAPTISM OF JESUS AND DEATH OF JOHN THE BAPTIST

At Jesus's baptism John recognised the immaculate personality of Jesus (John 1:34), and later, Jesus expressed thoughts which had no doubt occupied his mind for some time, of the transcendent nature of his future (Mark 1:14).

Even if there is no report, considering the relationship, John and Jesus are almost certain to have known each other in boyhood. John's exhortations (share food with those who do not have it, collect no more than the proper tax and, to soldiers, rob no one by violence or false accusation) were so popular that Herod Antipas feared political unrest (Luke 3:15). A pre-emptive arrest was made and John beheaded. The story of Salome asking for John's head after she had pleased Herod by dancing is a late addition intended to throw opprobrium on Herod (Matthew 14:6–11, Mark 6:22–27). Maybe John's fate was a warning not to challenge the secular authority. Shortly afterwards Jesus began his ministry.

To those who have had the excitement of seeing Gandhi, there is no difficulty in accepting that Simon and Andrew (Mark 1:18) and James and John (Mark 1:20) followed Jesus immediately and without question.

ATTITUDE OF JESUS'S FAMILY

Early in his ministry, Jesus's family, not understanding what was happening, became anxious about him and tried to restrain him. During this incident the famous question: 'Who are my mother and my brothers?' was asked (Matthew 12:46, Mark 3:33).

HEALING MIRACLES

In modern terms, sixteen of Jesus's healing miracles recorded in the Gospels* were of psychological or psychosomatic illness. Only three (Jairus's daughter, the man with dropsy and the bangled ear) were due to organic causes and these were resolved by physiological repair processes. Three were

---

*For reasons evident on page 219, the awakening of Lazarus is excluded.

malingering, the man by the pool at Bethesda, the blind
man and the demoniac boy. The question may be raised,
how permanent were the cures? The prevailing culture was
that disease was due to a failure to observe the minutiae
of the Mosaic code. Today, only the terminology has
changed. Failure of social and career ambitions stands
alongside degenerative and neoplastic diseases as a major
cause of illness. The understanding, sympathy and authority
of Christ supplied more than today's physicians can to
secure a remission. Even so, as an example, blindness of
hysterical origin cannot be considered cured today until the
propitus brings the fear to consciousness. Schizophrenia and
anxiety neurosis are long-term, possibly life-time, illnesses.
Inexplicable remissions occur after emotional stimulus such
as visits from friends.

Unclean spirit

In modern terms the man in the synagogue who cried out to
Jesus (Mark 1:23, Luke 4:33) was feeble-minded, bordering
on imbecility; that is with an intelligence quotient of ±50.
Such persons, if allowed to roam free (which in Western
countries they are not, as they upset the conscience of those
who see them but do not help), are found where people
congregate.

Comprehension is very limited and phrases they do not
understand are repeated aloud. Sudden and uncontrolled
movements of the limbs are frequent, simulating convulsions.
Depending on the cause of the mental deficiency, epileptic fits
may occur. Jesus's commanding presence imposed order on a
disordered mind.

Leprosy

The Gospels record two incidents in which Jesus cured
persons suffering from leprosy (see page 56). To a medical

mind the words: 'he stretched out his hand and touched him' (Matthew 8:3, Mark 1:41, Luke 5:13) are perhaps the most wonderful in the Bible. Biblical leprosy is a neuro-dermatitis; the power of Jesus's personality caused psychic tension to be replaced by calm.

Simon's mother-in-law

Probably Simon's (Simon Peter's) mother-in-law (Matthew 8:14, Mark 1:30, Luke 4:38) was suffering from a febrile cold or similar intercurrent infection. There is no evidence to support the idea that she may have had a recurrence of malaria. Aided by Jesus's personality, she 'made the effort' as people do when presented with a visitor.

The centurion's servant

The centurion living at Capernaum was a kind man, he cared about his servant who had become paralysed, and considered his house and hence himself to be unworthy of Jesus (Matthew 8:5, Luke 7:2). No medical comment can be made about the servant's paralysis except that the Greek, *paralutikos*, includes the meaning weakened or enfeebled, especially by a stroke. Even if humbly presented, there seems to have been a curious reluctance on the part of the centurion to let Jesus visit his house. The servant recovered without Jesus seeing him. The best guess is that he suffered from a transient ailment such as a faint, supervening on (and in part promoted by) cachexia of cancer, tuberculosis, anaemia (possibly due to a parasitic infection) or inadequate food.

The paralytic man

A crowd prevented entry to a house in Capernaum where Jesus was preaching, and so four men carrying a paralytic young man (he was addressed by Jesus as 'son') made a hole in the roof to gain access (Mark 2:4; Luke 5:18). Multiple sclerosis is a disease in which neurological symptoms (including paralysis) vary rapidly in severity and in location. Paralysis where symptoms relating to the central nervous system are due to oedema associated with a focal patch, before demyleination has proceeded beyond an early stage, often relieves itself very quickly and apparently completely. Roofs in the Middle East are flimsy and to make a hole in a roof is not the enormity it would be in the West. Even so, there is a suggestion of light-heartedness about this incident. Fortunately, euphoria is one of the symptoms of multiple sclerosis.

Multiple sclerosis may present itself at any age but most often in adolescence and early adulthood, affecting the sexes equally. The disease is commoner among persons who have spent their pre-adolescence in northern latitudes (or in the southern hemisphere in southern latitudes). This effect is genetic rather than environmental.

An alternative diagnosis is conversion hysteria. Conversion hysteria is one example of a dissociated state (see page 244) in which anxiety generated by an intolerable stimulus causes selective inhibition in the afferent side of the nervous system or paralysis in the motor side. The primary gain to the patient is avoidance of confrontation with the stressful stimulus and the secondary gain is often of value, e.g. sympathy. No clue is given to the intolerable situation; but in Israelite society there would have been many; possibly sin against the Mosaic code or risk of injury or death in a tribal dispute.

As its name implies, hysteria is commoner among women, particularly among the younger age groups, especially if they have a dependent personality. Most cases resolve spontaneously if the exciting stress is removed, but for those which do not, emotional support, sedation, analysis, hypnosis and even abreactive therapy may be required after due thought has been given to the desirability of removing a defensive mechanism. Authoritative reassurance by a respected figure is frequently effective in the numerous hysterical phenomena, often of a transitory nature, seen in general medical practice. Christ's 'take up your pallet and go home' (Mark 2:11) provides this need. There is no evidence, internal to this incident, to help in the differential diagnosis. As dramatic as recovery from multiple sclerosis can be on occasion, the young man's response was so quick that the preferred diagnosis must be conversion hysteria.

The man at Bethesda

Only John (5:2) recounts the cure of the man at the pool of Bethesda who was thought to have been paralysed for thirty-eight years. If this was correct, he was a fraud. Not only had he maintained life for that length of time, but lower limbs which had not been exercised for so long a period, from whatever cause, would not sustain walking. The original cause of the paresis may have been injury or arthritis, but the account, such as it is, suggests malingering. Starting as a deliberate and conscious process, after such a long time it would become built into the personality and, as with conversion hysteria, part of the efferent system of the brain would be suppressed.

The withered hand

In the synagogue, Jesus cured a man with a withered hand. The Greek for withered, *xērox*, is used of land which is parched or dried up. Lesions of the hand justifying such a term would be of long standing and this limits the possible cause (Matthew 12:14, Mark 3:1, Luke 6:6). Injury to nerves in the arm, in particular the musculo-spiral, median or ulnar nerves, gives paralysis, loss of sensation and deformity characteristic of each. Poliomyelitis in childhood is another possibility and injury at birth cannot be excluded. Loss of function would cause muscles to waste and interruption of the nerve supply would result in alteration of the pattern of the skin. Almost without exception, trick compensatory movements involving other muscles are developed and these can be very deceiving to the casual observer. Until modern micro-surgery, severed or severely damaged nerves virtually never recovered. Clinical details are minimal: if the lesion was in the forearm the limb might be held out using the muscles of the shoulder and back. Whatever this result may have been, the man's *élan vital* immeasurably improved. Perhaps a beggar of no consequence before, someone of importance had spoken to him, and, what is more, stuck up for him.

The Gerasene demon

The man living among the tombs (either natural or artificial caves) around Gerasene (Mark 5:2, Luke 8:26) was a Gentile, possibly a Greek as he went to the Decapolis. Very probably he was suffering from hepephrenia, a form of schizophrenia in which the sufferer appears to be absorbed in listening to bizarre voices and has violent physical outbursts. Emotional stimulation (such as would result from being addressed by Jesus) is known to result in improvement, at least for a short time. A cynic will say that the pigs ran away from the disturbance and noise of the proceedings. The pigs underwent a panic reaction which, before the cause of their fear became apparent to them, destroyed them.[3] Fear feeds on the fear of other individuals.

The power of Jesus's personality, which no one should forget, is illustrated in the story of the loaves and fishes (Matthew 14:13, Mark 6:37, Luke 9:10). Men on a day's outing, denied a free meal, were shamed into producing food secreted about their persons. Jesus declared all foods to be clean (Mark 7:19), *inter alia* increasing the potential availability of food in a land where, for many, it was scarce.

Jairus's daughter

Jairus's daughter, aged 12 years (Matthew 9:18, Mark 5:23, Luke 8:40), whose father thought she was dying, was in the prepubescent stage before the start of the adolescent spurt in growth, in which the hormone balance is unstable with possible effect on the vascular circulation. Left alone she would have recovered. Indeed, Jesus said: 'The child is not dead but sleeping.' It should be remembered that menarche in biblical times was almost certainly much later than today (see page 10).

The son of the widow of Nain

The son of the widow of Nain (Luke 7:11), stretched out on a bier and being carried out of the city to his grave, was probably suffering from catatonic schizophrenia (Greek *katatonein*, to stretch), which, as its name implies, is a form of schizophrenia in which the body, or parts of it, are maintained in bizarre postures. Often it is accompanied by stupor. Neurologically speaking, the abnormal behaviour is at a very high level and can be influenced by psychological factors such as Christ's presence. Rarely, catatonia may occur as an effect of cerebral tumour or of encephalitis.

Menstrual disturbance

Menstruation may be prolonged or excessive (as, for example, an excuse to avoid intercourse) or scanty. However, until organic disease has been excluded by thorough and repeated investigation, to ascribe disturbance to emotional changes is highly dangerous, the more so with bleeding at unexpected times. The woman who had 'suffered from a haemorrhage for twelve years' (Matthew 9:20, Mark 5:25, Luke 8:43) may have been suffering from menorrhagia (unpredictable

bleeding) before the menopause. Until recently, the observation that women living together (e.g. nuns) menstruated at
about the same time was explained by emotional influences,
but pheromones are now thought to be the cause. Be that
as it may, emotion has a marked influence on menstruation.
Aristotle (384–322 BC) gave the name *hustera* to the uterus
and thought that it was the seat of the emotions. 'Daughter,
your faith has made you well' (Mark 5:34) was literally true.
Jesus might well marvel at 'their unbelief' (Mark 6:6).

The daughter of the Syrophoenician woman

The Phoenician woman from Syria, a Greek speaking Gentile
(Matthew 15:22, Mark 7:26), probably of Greek extraction
or background as she kept dogs in her house,[4] whose child
was possessed by an unclean spirit, was suffering from
Munchausen's syndrome. Once thought to be rare, this condition is increasingly being reported. In it the patient simulates
on the conscious plane at first, but, as in malingering, he
enters the twilight bordering on the unconscious in order
to gain attention and affection. It is more common in men
than in women, but recently attention has been drawn to
women who suffer from vicarious Munchausen's syndrome
(often called Meadow's syndrome) by inventing in great detail
and over a long time symptoms and signs of disease in their
children.[5] Jesus gave the woman the assurance she sought;
without her and her dogs we should not have the glorious
phrase in the prayer of humble access in the Communion
Service: 'We are not worthy so much as to gather up the
crumbs under thy Table.'

The deaf man

The deaf man who was brought to Jesus also had an
impediment in his speech (Mark 7:35). Deaf persons
cannot 'speak plainly' unless they can hear or have heard

very recently. The diagnosis is conversion hysteria, starting as an escape from a situation which proved unacceptable. This account is reminiscent of the old theory that some speech defects were due to being tongue-tied because the frenum (a fold in the mucous membrane in the lower jaw connecting the underneath of the tongue to the floor of the mouth) was short. The Victorians failed to notice that cutting the frenum did not have much effect apart from confirming their belief.

The dumb demoniac

The Gospel account of the healing of the dumb demoniac (Matthew 9:32, Luke 11:14) cannot be supplemented by a history of illness or by clinical examination. As it is, the speed of the recovery of speech by the man excludes any diagnosis other than conversion hysteria, but this is not a wholly satisfactory way of making a diagnosis. Dumbness, whether deliberate or hysterical, is a convenient method of escaping having to make distasteful pronouncements.

The blind men

Jesus led aside the blind man from Bethsaida (Mark 8:22), a fishing village on the northern shore of the Sea of Galilee before healing him by touching him and spitting on his eyes. There may have been two other villages of the same name, but their sites cannot now be identified. If the report is true, the blind man gave himself away. In his excitement, he named trees and men, and so he must have seen them earlier.

In the account by John (9:1ff.) (whose medical veracity is, as will become apparent, questionable, see page 219) Jesus was in or near Jerusalem and the man he healed had been blind from birth. Because blindness was thought to be the result of sin, Jesus's disciples asked him who had sinned, the man or his parents, that he was born blind. Jesus answers by saying that he is the light of the world and illustrates this by giving light to the blind man. Strictly, blind from birth means born blind due to congenital disease. No form of congenital disease will respond to the application of clay even if made with spittle. A cure as quick as described by John would involve psychosomatic processes, thus disposing of the idea of blind from birth. More likely, the man suffered from scarring of the cornea due to ophthalmia neonatorum, inflammation of the conjunctivae and cornea through infection contracted during or soon after birth. In this respect gonococcal infection is particularly hazardous though it is by no means the only cause of scarring. Defective vision due to corneal scarring may seem to improve in the years to adolescence, though it must be said that marked improvement is rare. As recorded by John, who could embroider his stories, the man and his parents – which suggests that he had not attained adulthood – seem to protest too much, possibly under duress (on at least two occasions) by the Pharisees.

Conversion hysteria is unlikely to have been the cause of blindness in the two blind men (Matthew 9:27) cured when Jesus touched their eyes. The men were together and the causes of blindness in an unsanitised society (which in modern terms the Israelites were) are many. The stimulus provided by Jesus's interest might well have effected a feeling of apparent improvement. Indeed, Jesus himself said: 'According to your faith . . .'. Jesus made a similar remark to blind Bartimaeus sitting by the side of the road to Jericho (Mark 10:52, Luke 18:42). Both remarks are like those made by Jesus to the lepers (see page 56). A disordered psyche regained calm, to say that this was a conversion hysteria is perhaps too much. The mention of Timaeus, father of Bartimaeus, suggests an escape mechanism from over zealous parental care. A similar process may have operated when a blind and dumb demoniac was brought to Jesus (Matthew 12:22).

The causes of blindness are legion, trauma, infection, cataract, detachment of the retina and new growth, but an easily preventable cause is vitamin A deficiency. Many thousands, even millions, of children and adults suffer from corneal opaqueness due to vitamin A deficiency. A lack of this vitamin causes xerothalmia, a dryness of the corneal epithelium eventually resulting in ulceration and necrosis.

The demoniac boy

The first diagnosis which comes to mind about the boy with a dumb spirit and seizures (Mark 9:17, Matthew 17:14, Luke 9:37) is epilepsy. This presents difficulties. Excitatory epilepsy remits only after sophisticated and prolonged treatment with modern drugs. Even so the prognosis is uncertain. In his convulsion the boy is reported to have fallen into fire and water, but he is not reported as sustaining any injury. Contrary to commonly held beliefs epileptics suffer few injuries (possibly because they work in safe jobs) during fits. Not infrequently epilepsy is simulated and in such simulated attacks injury may be deliberately incurred. Also, there is no account of an aura or cry preceding the convulsion (both of which were known to the Babylonians in the seventh century BC),[6] nor of deep sleep after the convulsion, tongue biting, or urinary or faecal incontinence. Breath holding attacks (as in children in a tantrum) or hyperventilation (often in young adults) may, among other symptoms, produce seizures which may be difficult to distinguish from epilepsy. The evidence as recorded is contradictory, but the most likely diagnosis is feigned epilepsy. Whether simulation arises deliberately or from hysterical causes cannot be answered, but simulation of epileptic fits,[7] including the secondary signs as an attention-seeking device, is not difficult. Even *status-epilepticus*, a rare and dangerous complication of epilepsy in which convulsions become continuous, may be simulated.[8] *Status-epilepticus* requires urgent and vigorous treatment, which in the simulated form may be hazardous. A history of previous personality disorder is usual. Jesus's remark that the dumb spirit could 'not be driven out by anything but prayer' is significant.

The woman with a stoop

A woman for eighteen years had a 'spirit of infirmity' (Luke 13:11) which suggests she had psychiatric symptoms, possibly endogenous depression. Her bent back, carrying the sins of the world upon her shoulders, was an outward expression of her inward misery.

The man with dropsy

Dropsy is an accumulation of fluid in the intracellular space. Some form of back pressure in the venous system, may be involved which might result from thoracic or abdominal tumour, heart failure, cirrhosis of the liver or varicose veins. As air travellers know, tightness or swelling of the feet may occur if the legs are kept dependent for more than a short time. The man (Luke 14:2) seems to have got better quickly. Maybe he had been sitting on a wall with his legs hanging down. If this is so, Luke, who was a physician, should have known better than to record this as a healing incident.

The bangled ear

The ear has such a good blood supply that a bangled ear (that is one hanging down but not completely severed) (Luke 22:50) very often has sufficient blood supplied through the pedicle for healing to occur. Jesus replaced the ear of the High Priest's slave. A firm bandage would have helped. As with the man with dropsy (Luke 14:2), a cure was due to physiological processes.

THE TRANSFIGURATION

On Mount Tabor with Jesus at his transfiguration (Matthew 17:1, Mark 9:2, Luke 9:28) Peter and James experienced phantasy images[9] which arose from the total psychic situation. Such images, unlike hallucinations, never take the place of reality. Indeed, they have the capacity of achieving something beyond the verdict of the senses. This is not irrelevant to prayer (Mark 11:24).

DIVORCE, MARRIAGE AND ADULTERY

The Mosiac law (Deuteronomy 24:1) allowed a man in some circumstances to divorce his wife, but a wife was not allowed to divorce her husband. The law attempted (at the cost of injustice to the wife) to accommodate human frailty (Matthew 19:7, Mark 10:5). Jesus treats men and women equally (Matthew 19:9, Mark 10:11), but the one flesh created by joining in marriage 'let no man put asunder' (Matthew 19:6, Mark 10:9).

John, alone of the Gospels, reports Jesus's reaction when a woman taken in adultery is brought before him and he is asked whether the Mosaic punishment of death by stoning (see page 92) should be carried out. The narrative, a late addition to the Gospel, shows Jesus as merciful and compassionate: 'Let him who is without sin among you be the first to throw a stone at her' (John 8:7).

Stoning to death of a woman suspected or convicted of adultery is still practised today in some Muslim countries. Sahebjam[10] gives a horrifying account of this cruel and barbaric punishment carried out in a village in Iran in August 1986. The poor woman had not, in fact, committed adultery but was convicted at a meeting of the men of the village as a result of rumours spread by her husband who wanted to get rid of her. A deep hole was dug at the edge of the village square and the wretched victim was buried in this, standing upright, so that only her head and shoulders were visible. A circle was drawn round the hole and the men of the village stood round the circle with stones in their hands. The first stone was thrown by the victim's father, the next by her husband, then her two sons and finally all the men joined in. The mullah refused to allow her corpse to be buried in the village cemetery; it was taken outside the village on a cart and left by the river where it was eaten by dogs.

LAZARUS

The veracity of the report of raising Lazarus from the dead (John 11:1ff.) as an historical event is open to serious doubt.[11] No medical comment is called for. It may be worth while pointing out the incongruities in the story. Jesus said that Lazarus was asleep; in spite of Martha's fears that he would smell (as might be expected in that climate after four days) there is no report of this, and no human being, interred alive with full funeral rites in a closed tomb for four days would walk out, whether with help or not, except as a gibbering idiot.

GETHSEMANE

The crowd cheered Jesus on his way from Bethany and Bethphage to Jerusalem, but Jesus had known for some time that his fate in Jerusalem would be to be 'mocked and scourged and crucified' (Matthew 20:19). After an interval (traditionally four days) Jesus again expressed his fears at Gethsemane: 'My soul is very sorrowful, even to death' (Matthew 26:38). He sought strength in prayer, but the trouble he had with Peter, James and John, who had to be woken up three times, probably prevented sufficient concentration of attention for him to reach even a mild trance (dissociated state). His psyche must have been at full tension (with the consequent increase in adrenalin secretion which would stimulate the sympathetic system); even so, at his arraignment before the Sanhedrin and later before Pontius Pilate, he maintained considerable detachment.

THE ARREST OF JESUS

Jealousy is a powerful motive, especially when public esteem is involved (Mark 14:1). 'He has scattered the proud in the imagination of their hearts' (Luke 1:51). The priests thought Jesus's teaching, to which they tried to attach the offence of blasphemy, dangerous to the law upon which their status rested. When prescient overlay is discarded, the medical story of Jesus Christ's crucifixion is simple.[12] After a disturbed night at Gethsemane, he was roughed up and arraigned for ill-defined offences before the Sanhedrin. The Sanhedrin was composed of six representatives of each of the twelve tribes of Israel and numerous servants were attached to it; to say the least, it was a hostile tribunal. As the proceedings developed, vague charges against Roman law were added.[13] Jesus was judged to merit death and for this reason was delivered to Pontius Pilate.

The Gospels are inconsistent regarding the timing of Jesus's appearance before the Sanhedrin. Most likely Jesus was detained late at night and appeared before the Sanhedrin (possibly an emergency meeting) very early in the morning. His appearance before Pilate was 'at daybreak', i.e. before 0600 hours local time. One cannot but remark at the ineptness in asking for crucifixion, for death could not normally be expected to take place before sunset on Friday, Saturday being the Jewish Sabbath. Pilate 'perceived that it was out of envy that the chief priests had delivered him up' (Mark 15:10). Endeavouring to remove the risk of future blame, Pilate consulted Herod Antipas, who happened to be in Jerusalem that day, as Jesus, being a Galilean, was nominally under Herod's jurisdiction. Herod offered no opinion and returned Jesus to Pilate, with the result that

Herod and Pilate became firm friends, having previously been enemies (Luke 23:12). In a final attempt to avoid condemning Jesus, Pilate called upon the crowd who had assembled to express an opinion whether Jesus or Barabbas, a condemned criminal, should be released. The inevitable result was a cry for Jesus's death.

CROWD BEHAVIOUR

As McDougall[14] points out, 'participation in group life degrades the individual, assimilating his mental process to those of the crowd whose brutality, inconsistency and unreasoning impulsiveness have been the theme of many writers'. Penrose's monograph on crowd behaviour is seminal.[3] Among a crowd of persons voting indifferently, a relatively few persons consistently control the decisions. If the crowd before Pilate (Mark 15:8) was 1000 persons, 32 votes would make it 84 per cent certain, 64 votes 98 per cent certain and 96 votes 99 per cent certain that Jesus was crucified (see Table 5). The High Priest would have no difficulty in packing the crowd (see page 220).

THE FLOGGING OF JESUS

All condemned persons were subject to flogging, and Roman flogging was no mean thing. Whether Jesus was flogged in the hope that this would satisfy the crowd (John 19:1ff.), or as part of the crucifixion routine (Matthew 27:26, Mark 15:15), or as a gesture by Pilate to Herod (Luke 23:16) is immaterial. Four or five braided thongs of leather in which lead balls and pieces of sheep bone were incorporated produced major laceration all over the back and legs sufficient to cause substantial loss of blood and fluid. Each thong would denude the skin and subcutaneous tissues (which would expose the nerve endings) to bare the underlying muscles so as to be the equivalent of a third or fourth degree burn. Serious loss of blood and fluid would start and, quite apart from the shock due to pain, volaemic shock would be imminent. Blood pressure would be low, the electrolyte balance grossly disturbed, kidney function diminished and fluid accumulating in the intracellular space. Later, accumulation of fluid in body cavities would start. Both Primrose[15] and Bucklin[16] have confused Roman practice and Jewish law in supposing that Jesus was flogged, at any rate in part, on the chest and abdomen. Transgressors against the Mosaic law were punished in the Temple by the priest using a three-pronged leather whip made of calf hide. The number of strokes was restricted to not more than forty, in practice thirty-nine; one-third were given on the chest and two-thirds on the shoulder.[17] No doubt it was this form of chastisement that the Apostles had in mind when they said that they suffered stripes.

THE PRAETORIUM

After the flogging Jesus was taken to the Praetorium (Mark 15:16) forming part of the Antonia barracks, now the convent of the Sisters of Sion. Some of the paving stones etched to make a playboard for games popular with the garrison are in place today. Once a year it was the practice to parade a condemned person for the soldiers to play with. A whole battalion (600 men) was called together to amuse themselves by taunting Jesus. No witness exists to what happened in the Praetorium[18] and the bland reports in the Gospels may be due to the absence of witnesses to what went on in the barrack-room. Undoubtedly brutality was the order of the day, even to crowd in 600 men would lead to ribald jostling. The soldiers clothed Jesus in a purple cloak, put a crown of thorns on his head and a reed (Greek *kalamos*) in his hand to indicate kingship. Roman rulers, including the Emperor, did not carry sceptres or wear crowns. However, the army in Judaea was composed of auxiliary troops, *auxilia*, who were

Table 5. Number of bloc votes to control decisions in a crowd of 1000. Penrose[3]

Number in indifferent crowd	Number in controlling group of bloc votes		
1000	32	64	95
Percentage of decisions carried by bloc voters	84.1	97.7	99.9

not of Italian origin. Jews were exempt from military service. The Gospels say that Jesus was struck on the head with the reed, but *kalamos* can also mean something manufactured from reeds. This can be as small as a quill or as substantial as a staff. Whatever was made in this case was sufficient to imitate a sceptre. Considering the brutality which might be expected from Roman levies, this was a comparatively minor assault. Most probably Jesus was standing up when he faced his adversaries and at this point his psyche and soma would have been reduced to a low ebb.

As intended, Jesus was severely weakened by the flogging and further weakened by assaults in the Praetorium. He was unable to carry the crosspiece (*patibulum*) of the Cross, which if made of hardwood and measuring 7 feet (2.1 m) x 6 inches (15 cm) x 4 inches (10 cm) would weigh about 48 lb (22 kg), the 700 yards (0.64 km) to Golgotha. As the sites of the Holy Places cannot be identified with certainty, distances are approximate. (See figure 7). As those condemned to crucifixion were expected to carry the *patibulum*, they were presumably able to do so. Contrary to what the Gospels suggest, the vertical (*stipes*) of the Cross was kept permanently in place.

CRUCIFIXION

Crucifixion was reserved for slaves but could also be inflicted on any person who could not prove Roman citizenship.

Many Romans protested at its cruelty: Cicero[19] called it *'crudelissimum taeterrimumque supplicium'* (the most cruel and abominable punishment). Crucifixion was invented by the Persians, introduced into Egypt by Alexander the Great and refined by the Romans to produce an excruciatingly painful and prolonged death. Constantine abolished it in AD 315.[20]

No doubt wishing to show the glory of the Saviour, artists and sculptors raise the Cross upwards towards the sky and usually show Jesus with a seraphic smile of comfortable death, even though they believed that he endured the full agony. In fact the crucified were raised only about a foot or 18 inches (30 – 40 cm) above the ground (so that conversation, if it could be sustained, would be possible). Nailing of the forearms to the *patibulum* was through the wrist (nailing through the palms would not 'hold') and this was done on the ground. A flange of wood prevented the nail head pulling through the flesh. Only exceptionally would the nails driven through the forearm above the wrist avoid severe damage to the median nerve. Jesus seems to have been spared this and the consequent agonising flashes of pain along the arms. The victim was raised to the vertical position and the *patibulum* completed the cross when inserted into a slot in the *stipes*. It was held in place by ropes or nails. A small projection, a *sedile*, supported the buttocks. Death occurred from slow asphyxia due to increasing inability to work the respiratory muscles, in spite of the most desperate efforts, against the force of gravity pulling the body organs downwards. Two, three or even four days elapsed before death finally ensued.

When Jesus was crucified, the use of the *suppendaneum* under the feet was unusual and the knees were twisted for the nailing of the feet to the *stipes*, probably between the tibia and the Achilles tendon. The *suppendaneum* gave some support to the feet and thus slightly reduced the gravitational thrust of the body with consequent help to the respiratory muscles. The respiratory muscles had to work against the downward pull of the body during inspiration; expiration, normally passive, also required muscular effort. Speaking is done in expiration and on the cross special effort would be called for. Gradually the muscles would become exhausted until agonising effort was needed to obtain the tiniest gasp of air. Breaking the legs, whether the thigh or lower leg, would remove such support as there was to the body from the lower limbs. In addition the shock, especially if the thigh was broken, might alone cause death to supervene. Breaking the legs was not done for any kindly reason. When the supposed corpse was removed from the cross, it was thrown into a trench. Should recovery occur, and the practice suggests that this was a recognised possibility, the victim was unable to avoid being devoured by wild animals.

Haas[21] reports on the bony remains, found near Nablus, of a man crucified between the end of the second century BC and AD 70. Religious reburial limited the time available for preservation and examination. The right tibia (shin bone) and the left fibula and tibia were broken. A nail transfixed both calcanei which, when found, were adherent. Haas concludes that the lower limb had been twisted to the right so the right lower limb was next to the *stipes*. Remains of a piece of wood were found below the nail, presumably to prevent the nail 'pulling through'. Subsequent examination led Zias and Sekeles[22] to disagree with details of Haas's report, most importantly the break in the left tibia was possibly due to the fragile nature of the remains.

Lindars[23] wonders if the two men crucified one on each side of Jesus, had been crucified some time before. An assumption can be made that being near death (though still able to speak) but not yet dead, they had their legs broken (John 19:32).

CALVARY

Based on Proverbs 31:6, 'Give strong drink to him who is perishing', Jesus was offered, but refused, a sponge soaked in sour wine (vinegar) containing a decoction of myrrh (Mark 15:36). Sometimes a decoction of mandrake (which contains hyoscine) was added.[24]

Mark (15:25) says that Jesus was crucified at the third hour (0900 hours) but John (19:14) implies some time after the sixth hour (1200 hours). The Jewish day starts at sunset which means that to conform to the Mosaic law, Jesus's death had to be secured before sunset on Friday (Saturday being the Jewish Sabbath). Matthew and Luke agree that there was darkness from the sixth hour (1200 hours) to the ninth hour (1500 hours). This is also mentioned in the non-canonical Gospel of Nicodemus.[2] According to the apocryphal Gospel of Peter[2] the Jews were worried lest the sun should set and Jesus be still alive. At the ninth hour Mark (15:34) and Matthew (27:46) agree that Jesus cried: 'My God, my God, why hast thou forsaken me?'. Luke (23:46) and John (19:30) quote different words: 'Father, into thy hands I commit my spirit' and 'it is finished', but the sense is the same. 'And Jesus uttered a loud cry, and breathed his last' (Mark 15:37); 'And Jesus cried again with a loud voice and yielded up his spirit' (Matthew 27:50). The spectators were in no doubt that this was the moment of death and went home (Luke 23:48). Edwards, Gabel and Hosmer[25] interpret the cry as suggesting a catastrophic terminal event, but equally it may have been a cry of dereliction,[26] a loud expiration which often precedes syncope. Among Edwards, Gabel and Hosmer's[25] horrific illustrations is one of the spear thrust, an event which, for reasons given below, did not take place.

So far as the record goes, only one disciple, possibly John, was at the crucifixion (John 19:26), but Mary, Jesus's mother, Mary Magdalene and Mary, the wife of Clopas, were present. Jesus's personality was strong, with little concern for himself, but a feeling of being forsaken, abandoned and alone would be justified.

According to Mark (15:44), Pilate, surprised that Jesus

had died so quickly, 'wondered if he were already dead' and enquired of the centurion present at the crucifixion before giving permission for the body to be taken down.

A centurion was a seasoned soldier who had been promoted from the ranks and could be aged anything between 30 and 60 years. He would have had a primary education, be very competent and familiar with death. Polybius[27] describes the character of centurions thus: 'Centurions are desired not to be bold and adventurous so much as good leaders, of steady and prudent mind, not prone to take the offensive or start fighting wantonly, but able when overwhelmed and hard-pressed to stand fast and die at their post.' Nevertheless, the centurion was mistaken in saying that Jesus was dead, if that is what he did say (see page 233). The two who were crucified with Jesus had their legs broken (John 19:32); this would increase shock but not necessarily kill them. In his regard for Jesus (Matthew 27:54, Luke 23:47) the centurion may have wished to avoid further indignity to a 'corpse'.

As the site of the crucifixion and that of the Antonia palace cannot be fixed precisely (see Figure 7), it must be assumed that up to two hours may have elapsed before Jesus was removed from the Cross (Matthew 27:58, Mark 15:46, Luke 23:53, John 19:38). An important omission from the Gospels is the names of those who helped Joseph of Arimathea with this. The only information we have is from the apocryphal Acts of Pilate[2] that twelve men who did not believe in the virgin birth helped him.

BLOOD AND WATER

Alone of the Gospels, John reports that Jesus's side was pierced with a spear (John 19:34), probably a thin one,[28] and 'at once there came out blood and water'. If this is true, it indicates that Jesus was alive, even if only at the sub-clinical level. John has spoilt his reliability as a medical

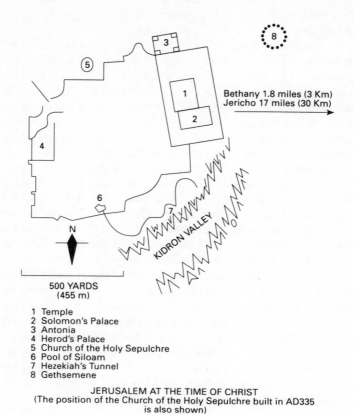

1 Temple
2 Solomon's Palace
3 Antonia
4 Herod's Palace
5 Church of the Holy Sepulchre
6 Pool of Siloam
7 Hezekiah's Tunnel
8 Gethsemene

JERUSALEM AT THE TIME OF CHRIST
(The position of the Church of the Holy Sepulchre built in AD335
is also shown)

Figure 7 Diagram of Jerusalem at the time of Christ.

witness by introducing the story of the raising of Lazarus from
the dead (see page 219); currently, this is widely accepted
to be a fabrication and no other Gospel records what must
have been a most dramatic incident. The story of doubting
Thomas (John 20:24) also falls flat.

Unless the soldier was indulging in casual spite, there was no motive for the thrust except to confirm death, but, if John's account is true, it did the reverse. It is unlikely that any of the Apostles were present,[10] but John protests (perhaps too much) that a truthful witness saw the spear pierce Jesus's side (John 19:35).

Makers of religious memorabilia place the wound from the spear on the right chest. In fact we have no knowledge of where it was. Wilkinson[28] emphasises this but accepts previous tentative suggestions that it was on the left side. Wilkinson points out that the Greek *exagō* does not suggest that the blood and water came out with any force but equally that the blood was more than an insignificant ooze. Jesus must have been alive as corpses do not bleed. The first person to notice this was Origen[29] (*c*. AD 185–254). Edwards, Gabel and Hosmer[25] accept unsubstantiated tradition about the chest to the right of the sternum as the place of the wound and in addition assume wrongly that the order of words in Greek, i.e. blood and water, indicates prominence rather than sequence in time. With such a strong pathological input to their paper it is surprising that they appear to accept that Jesus was dead when the spear thrust was made. They also accept that in some circumstances the flood of blood and water may have been substantial.

Cameron[30] suggests that acute dilation of the stomach due to shock was present. Rendle Short[31] inclines to this view. Both believe that the blood and water originated when the stomach was pierced. John uses the Greek *pleura*, which originally meant the rib of a human being, then the side of a human being or animal, but by 150 BC was applied to a side in general terms, e.g. the side of a ship, river or triangle. The pleural sac covering the lung extends downwards to just above the lower ribs. A major thrust through the rib cage would be catastrophic, a pneumothorax with displacement of the mediastinum (including the heart) would be immediate. Lower than this, dramatic bleeding (but no water) from the liver on the right or from the spleen on the left would ensue.

A simple explanation is that the blood came from the wound in the chest wall and the 'water' from fluid in the pleural cavity with a small self-sealing lesion in the parietal pleura. An even simpler (and therefore more likely) explanation is that the soldier's action was an idle and motiveless poke of the spear at a scab or bleb resulting from the flogging. John had already said that Jesus was dead (19:33) so there was no motive for the spear thrust, unless the soldier struck Jesus out of spite or casual cruelty. John's story seems to have been introduced to emphasise Jesus's supra-natural nature and has little historicity. Primrose[15] was wrong in supposing that Jesus was flogged on the abdomen and sternum, which would permit accumulation of fluid in the abdomen (ascites) (see page 221). He thinks that the blood and water flowing from Jesus's side referred to by John (19:34) came from the abdomen.

MEDICAL CAUSE OF DEATH

Attempts to postulate the medical cause of Jesus's apparent death appear to have begun with Stroud[32] in 1847. After considering sheer exhaustion he concludes that the desperate agony of Gethsemane renewed on the Cross, caused rupture of the heart, but at the same time he discuss sympathetically whether Jesus dismissed his spirit. In 1887 Risdon Bennett[33] believed Jesus's sudden death was due to 'rupture of the heart from agony of mind', possibly aggravated by piercing the side with a spear.

Neither Primrose[15] nor Wilkinson[26] discuss the ordeal of being the plaything of a battalion of soldiers. If blows from the staff were not confined to the head, injuries to other parts of the body may have been inflicted.

Jesus spent six hours on the Cross, a comparatively short time, and was taken down to a cool place.

SYNCOPE

From the moment he was flogged, Jesus was in a state of shock. Severe pain would continue and though blood would have been lost from the lacerations on Jesus's back, dilation of the small blood vessels (where the confluence of the arterioles and venules form a plexus supplying the tissues) would be most important in reducing the quantity of blood returned to the heart. In addition, blood electrolytes would be disturbed (possibly to the point of incipient renal failure). Delayed concussion does not occur but shock rather than the blow on the head may have confused mentation.

Even if the weather in April was not particularly warm, especially as for three hours before presumed death the sun was obscured (Mark 15:33), being fixed in the upright position for about six hours would not be lethal but would not assist blood supply to the brain. Jesus's collapse was due to hypotension. However, so long as the supply of oxygen to the brain is maintained, even at minimal level, (bowing the head would reduce the height that blood had to be raised) recovery is to be expected. This is the difference between clinical death and brain death. Primrose,[15] who in 1949 was senior anaesthetist at Glasgow Royal Infirmary, thought Jesus may not have died on the Cross but suffered the experience of dying, with 'the somatic activities having been maintained at a very low level from which recovery took place as soon as conditions came to favour this'.

In 1890, Clark,[34] a physician practising in Oswego in New York State, forestalled much of the present discussion by suggesting that the physical cause of the 'death' (Clark used this word) of Jesus was hypotension. Remarkably, having regard to the mores of the time, Clark went on 'Removed to the cool tomb by the tender hands of his friends, and placed in a horizontal position, he recovered, probably after some hours, from his state of syncope ... and easily made his way to some selected refuge ...' Clark suggested that Mary [Magdalene] mistook the funeral linen for the angels clad in white.

The appearance of the victim of hypotension is difficult to describe: the skin is ashen white and pulse and respiration are imperceptible. In 1965 Bourne,[35] senior anaesthetist at St Thomas's Hospital, giving expression to ideas he had had for ten years, wrote that 'not even the deepest coma so closely resembles death'. He was sympathetic to the idea originating in the United States in 1935 that death from crucifixion was usually due to fainting. Here, terminology becomes important. To the lay mind, fainting implies a transitory state of a feeling of giddiness; loss of consciousness, if it occurs, is for a few seconds. The subject falls into the horizontal position and consciousness returns. If the subject is prevented from falling, fainting is dangerous. The medical mind becomes concerned if the low blood pressure which caused the faint persists and the brain is starved in varying degree of blood and oxygen. When these are restored, recovery follows provided the oxygen to the brain has been maintained above a critical level. Usually, this is quick, but if the fall in blood pressure has been severe may be delayed for hours or days. The heart is a pump whose function is to deliver blood to the tissues and critically to the brain. The output depends on the power of the heart muscle and the return of blood from the tissues. A weakened heart, further embarrassed by reduced volume of blood from the tissues because of dilation of the small blood vessels, is unable to raise blood to maintain an adequate supply to the brain. The height blood has to be raised to reach the brain is crucial.

Today, a physician faced with the same diagnostic problem as the centurion, would ask for an electrocardiogram (trace of electric currents associated with the beat of the heart) and, if available, want an electroencephalogram (trace of electrical activity of the brain). He would be very foolish not to consult senior colleagues.

Later, Bourne[36] in evidence to the High Court described fainting consequent upon a sudden fall in blood pressure when a patient was anaesthetised in an upright position. Recovery ensues when patients are laid flat; usually this was quick, but occasionally some hours, days and in one case two weeks elapsed before consciousness and apparent normality was regained, depending on how long the fall in blood pressure and the upright position had lasted. The centurion who was asked by Pontius Pilate whether Jesus was dead was neither trained nor equipped to make a diagnosis; he had every reason to say what he did.

Wilkinson[26] points out the need to explain Jesus's early death (which incidentally rules out Le Bec's[37] theory of asphyxia) and notes that the different Greek verbs used by the authors of the Gospels to describe Jesus's presumed death imply voluntary surrender of life; he suggests that the cry Jesus gave was one of dereliction. Mark and Luke used *exepneusen* (he breathed out), Matthew *aphēken* (he sent forth, let go) and John *paredōken* (he delivered up, handed over). In Jesus's case, diminished cerebral circulation due to shock and postural hypotension caused syncope, to which was added, though not critically, confused mentation. Paradoxically, the assaults Jesus received in the Praetorium saved his life.

Some individuals, probably because of liability to venous pooling and increased sympathetic drive in the balance between sympathetic and vagal nervous systems are susceptible to hypotension.

THE EMPTY TOMB

All four Gospels record that Pilate gave Jesus's body to Joseph of Arimathea (a member of the Sanhedrin who voted against committal), who placed Jesus in the tomb being prepared against his own demise (Matthew 27:60). Being taken down from the Cross would have caused pain, and we may speculate that this stimulus caused Jesus to give signs of life. Jesus was laid horizontally in a cold place, possibly in the tomb, so that cerebral circulation was restored.

When the women failed to find Jesus's body in the tomb, the Gospels agree on one point only: the stone in front of the entrance was rolled away. Matthew (28:1ff.) and Mark (16:1ff.) say that an angel or a young man said: 'He is not here'. Luke (24:1ff.) reports the presence of two men who asked the question: 'Why do you seek the living among the dead?'. John (20:12) says that Mary Magdalene saw two angels in the tomb who asked: 'Woman, why are you weeping?' As she departed, she questioned a man, whom she first thought to be the gardener, but later addressed as Jesus. In Matthew (28:9) Jesus appeared to the two women as they left the tomb. According to Luke (24:11), the reports of the women as to what happened at the tomb were not believed by the rest of the Apostles.

From the point of view of hypotension alone, Jesus would be able to walk as soon as the blood supply to the brain had been restored. The trauma of the nails would not prevent this.

The empty tomb story is of no significance as evidence for or against the Resurrection, for the discovery that a tomb is empty does not of itself point to the conclusion that the body which once lay in it has been reanimated. Lindars[38] demonstrates that the story of the empty tomb arose from belief in the bodily resurrection of Jesus and should not be argued as the origin of that belief.

No one knows what happened after Jesus was crucified. Those who prefer alternative hypotheses must a) explain Jesus's early and unexpected collapse on the Cross and consider the significance of this in the light of the medical knowledge of the time. b) if Jesus was placed in the tomb, which according to Matthew (27:65) was, at Pilate's command guarded by soldiers, explain how he escaped or how his body was removed. If he was dead, how did the Romans and the Sanhedrin, both of whom had all-pervading intelligence, fail to find the body? The advantage that would accrue from doing so, or even of saying that they had, would be enormous. c) consider the possibility that the whole episode was planned so that early removal from the Cross might be secured; if the conclusion is that this was done, admire Jesus's courage. d) accept that, if John's account of the issue of blood (19:34) is correct, Jesus did not die from the effects of crucifixion but from the spear thrust.

APPEARANCES OF JESUS

The primary tradition of the post-Crucifixion appearances of Jesus is to be found in I Corinthians 15:5 – 8. Writing in about AD 53 – 54, St Paul says: 'And that he appeared to Cephas, then to the twelve. Then he appeared to more than five hundred brethren at one time, most of whom are still alive, though some have fallen asleep. Then he appeared to James, then to all the apostles. Last of all, as to one untimely born, he appeared also to me.' It is important to note that Paul uses the same verb ōphthē, 'he was seen' to describe all these appearances. This verb, besides meaning objective sighting, also carries the meaning of to see with the mind, perceive, experience. No possibility of a physical appearance arises in the case of Paul on the road to Damascus (Acts 9:1 – 9) and he must have thought that the other appearances were in the same category. Paul's own account of his experience (Galatians 1:16) is tantalisingly brief.

When Paul's account is compared with the Gospel stories many discrepancies are apparent. The Gospels give some support to a special appearance to Peter (Mark 16:7, Luke 24:34), and the appearances to the twelve (or more accurately the eleven, Judas having been removed) are dealt with in Matthew 28:1ff., Luke 24:33–51 and John 20:19–23, 26–29. The Gospels contain no reference to the appearance to 500 brothers at once, or to the appearance to James, Jesus's brother. There is, however, a reference to the appearance to James in the apocryphal Gospel according to the Hebrews.[2] The post-Crucifixion stories in the Gospels are more colourful and circumstantial, though conflicting. They describe a risen body which can appear and vanish and pass through doors, yet eats and drinks. The Gospel accounts may be independent of the primary tradition set down by Paul, or it may be that Paul's account was retold and interpreted before being written in the Gospels and that the natural tendency to embellish the story was influenced by the pressures of controversies within the early Church.

Jesus's appearances, whether real or supposed, are not compelling evidence for or against resurrection or resuscitation. They are merely a statement of the fact that, after the Crucifixion, certain persons believed they had seen Jesus again. There can be no doubt that they were profound religious experiences. The vivid impressions left by the appearances added to memories of Jesus's life and character resulted in the amazing vitality and inspiration of earliest Christianity.

In the hours, days and weeks following Jesus's supposed death, the disciples and the women must have been under intense psychological pressure far beyond the capacity of their brains to cope emotionally. Individual and corporate mental images, but not visualisations, were to be expected. In terms of Pavlov's dogs, they underwent a transmarginal inhibition, a state of activity of the brain in which hysterical suggestibility (or alternatively counter-suggestibility) frequently occurs.[39] Battle fatigue or brain-washing is analogous. Reliving their experiences relieved emotion. The disciples and the women underwent an abreaction and thereby gained calm and certainty (see page 244).

Rees[40] (a general medical practitioner in Wales) reported

that nearly half of bereaved spouses had hallucinations, i.e. mental images, of their dead partner. The hallucinations lasted for many years, sometimes longer than ten years. In England, persons or partners with occupations classified as Groups I and II by the Registrar-General were reported as most affected.[41] The disciples would fall into these groups.

SUMMARY

The abuse meted out to Jesus in the Praetorium led to his collapse due to hypotension, early removal from the Cross and resuscitation. Individual and corporate suggestibility among the disciples and the women explain the reports of subsequent appearances. This hypothesis accepts the historical events surrounding the Crucifixion and resurrection appearances of Jesus but explains them in terms acceptable to the modern mind.

References

1. Bostock G. Virgin Birth or Human Conception? *Expository Times*. 1986, 97: 260.
2. James M.R. (ed.) *The Apocryphal New Testament*. Oxford: Clarendon Press, 1926.
3. Penrose L.S. *On the Objective Study of Crowd Behaviour*. London: H.K. Lewis, 1952.
4. Dufton F. The Syrophoenician Woman and her dogs. *Expository Times*. 1989, 100: 417.
5. Anon. Meadow and Munchausen. *Lancet*. 1983, i: 456.
6. Kernier Wilson J.V., Reynold E.H. Translation and analysis of a Cuneiform Text forming part of a Babylonian Treatise on Epilepsy. *Medical History*. 1990, 34: 185.
7. Hopkins A. Epilepsy: *Oxford Textbook of Medicine,* ed. Weatherall D.J., Ledingham J.S.G., Warrell D.A. Oxford: Oxford University Press, 1988.
8. Anon. Pseudostatus epilepticus. *Lancet*. 1989, ii: 485.
9. Jung C.G. *Psychological Types*. London: Routledge & Kegan Paul, 1953.
10. Sahebjam F. *La Femme Lapidée*. Paris: Grasset, 1990.

11. Barrett C.K. *The Gospel According to St John.* London: SPCK, 1978.

12. Lloyd Davies M., Lloyd Davies T.A. Resurrection or resuscitation? *Journal of the Royal College of Physicians 1991,* **25**: 167.

13. Watson F. Why was Christ crucified? *Theology.* 1985, **88**: 105.

14. McDougall W. *The Group Mind.* Cambridge: Cambridge University Press, 1920.

15. Primrose W.B. A Surgeon looks at the Crucifixion. *Hobart Journal.* 1948, **47**: 387.

16. Bucklin R. The Legal and Medical Aspects of the Trial and Death of Christ. *Science and Law.* 1970, **10**: 14.

17. Danby H. (ed.) *The Mishnah,* trans. from the Hebrew. Oxford: Oxford University Press, 1933.

18. Thompson J.A. *The Bible and Archaeology.* Exeter: Paternoster Press, 1976.

19. Cicero. *In Verrem,* V.64. The Verrine Orations. Loeb Classical Library. London: Heinemann, 1928–35.

20. Mommsen Th., Meyer P.M. (eds.) *Codex Theodosianus.* IV.40.2: Berlin: 1905.

21. Haas N. Anthropological Observations on the Skeletal Remains from Giv'at ha Mitvar. *Israel Exploration Journal.* 1970, **20**: 38.

22. Zias J., Sekeles E. The Crucified Man from Giv'at ha Mitvar: A Reappraisal. *Israel Exploration Journal,* 1985, **35**: 22.

23. Lindars B. *The Gospel of John.* London: Oliphants, 1972.

24. Hollman A. Herbal Remedies and Physic Gardens. *The Oxford Companion to Medicine,* ed. Walton J., Beeson P.B., Bodley Scott R. Oxford: Oxford University Press, 1986.

25. Edwards W.D., Gabel W.J., Hosmer F.E. On the Physical Death of Jesus Christ. *Journal of the American Medical Association,* 1986, **255**: 1455.

26. Wilkinson J. The Physical Cause of the Death of Jesus Christ. *Expository Times.* 1972, **83**: 104.

27. Polybius. *Histories* VI, 24. Loeb Classical Library. London: Heinemann, 1922–27.

28. Wilkinson J. The Incident of the Blood and Water in John 19:34. *Scottish Journal of Theology.* 1975, **28**: 149.

29. Origen. *Contra Celsum,* trans. Chadwick H. Cambridge: Cambridge University Press, 1953.

30. Cameron, J.L. *The Gospel According to St John,* summarised by Tasker R.G.V. London: Tyndale Press, 1960.

31. Rendle Short A. *The Bible and Modern Medicine.* London: Paternoster Press, 1953.

32. Stroud W. *Treatise on the Physical Cause of the Death of Jesus Christ and its relation to the Principles and Practice of Christianity.* London: Hamilton & Adams, 1847.

33. Risdon Bennett J. *The Diseases of the Bible.* London: Religious Tract Society, 1887.

34. Clark C.C.P. What was the Physical Cause of the Death of Jesus Christ? *Medical Record (NY),* 1890: Nov.15, 543.

35. Bourne J. The Resurrection of Christ: a remarkable medical theory. *Sunday Times.* London: 24 January 1965.

36. Bourne J. Fainting theory of Crucifixion. *British Medical Journal.* 1972, ii: 310.

37. Le Bec P. *La Passion de Notre Seigneur Jesus Christ selon le Chirurgien,* trans. Earl of Wicklow. Garden City, New York: Doubleday Image Books, 1953.

38. Lindars B. Jesus Risen: Bodily Resurrection but No Empty Tomb. *Theology.* 1986, **89**: 90.

39. Sargant W. *The Mind Possessed.* London: Heinemann, 1973.

40. Rees W.D. The Hallucination of Widowhood. *British Medical Journal.* 1971, **4**: 37.

41. Parker M.C., Benjamin B., Fitzgerald M.G. Broken Heart: a Statistical Study of Increased Mortality among Widowers. *British Medical Journal.* 1969, i: 740.

22

THE ACTS OF THE APOSTLES

APPEARANCES OF JESUS

The Acts, whose authorship is traditionally attributed to Luke, say that Jesus presented himself to the Apostles on many occasions over a period of forty days (1:3). The probability that these appearances were not due to Jesus's physical presence but to mental perceptions, no doubt very compelling to the Apostles, is discussed on pages 235 and 244. Whether in writing the Gospels the authors chose words with the care that would justify subsequent semantic analysis may be questioned. Writing about the Ascension, Luke uses the Greek *blepontōn* (1:9), which, among other meanings, can be interpreted as 'looking on'. Visualisation of Jesus, consequent upon his physical presence, cannot be assumed.

THE ASCENSION

Whilst he was on the Mount of Olives (height 330 feet, 100 m) 'a cloud took him [Jesus] out of their [the Apostles'] sight' (1:9). In that area rapid changes of climate are usual and a morning mist is not uncommon.[1] For this account to be true, it does not necessarily mean that the physical Jesus was lost in a cloud, but that this was the Apostles' perception. By now the Apostles had been under strain for forty days, their emotions simply ran out and this was a psychologically satisfying place for them to do so. Bethany, the home of Martha and Mary, friends of Jesus, where he had stayed in the past, is about a mile and three quarters (3 km) from Jerusalem, on the far side of the Mount of Olives (which in fact is a ridge rather than a single peak). Mark (11:1) refers to 'Bethphage and Bethany, at the Mount of Olives' and Matthew to 'Bethphage, to the Mount of Olives' (21:1). Jesus started his journey to Jerusalem from Bethphage, which is only a few minutes' walk from Bethany.

THE GIFT OF TONGUES

The tower of Babel (Genesis 11:1), one of the many towers of Babylon, was, according to legend, built in the plain of Shinar without the approval of the Lord. Until then there was one language, but in a fit of pique the Lord made it difficult after that for men to understand their neighbours. Very probably the story is a polytheistic myth.

Because people were affected, the gift of tongues (2:2) requires medical consideration. Peter may have known Latin and all the disciples probably knew some Greek as well as Hebrew and Aramaic. An abnormal storm with winds and lightning caused much excitement. In Britain today there are many dialects (Glaswegian, Geordie, Liverpudlian, Devonian) which are not mutually intelligible, but when the listener is alert, sense can with ease be made of them. The Holy Spirit also caused a jabber of words in Ephesus (19:6). Very probably there was a lot of shouting, distorted by the noise of the storm. The senseless repetition of words or phrases occurs in Alzheimer's disease, schizophrenia and autism, but that would not account for the babel.

DYSENTERY

There is a strong implication that the man who bought the field (1:18) was Judas, though Matthew (27:5) says that he hanged himself. After buying the field the man was seized with dysentery, probably amoebic, as besides much bleeding prolapse of the rectum may occur in severe or chronic cases. With symptoms like this he is likely to have died.

ABREACTION

The Apostles were very frightened of the possible response of the authorities to their teaching; indeed, they had cause to be as Peter and John were arrested and taken before the Sanhedrin (4:1). Together with the women they continued to discharge their emotion by prayer, to find that their anxieties were trivial compared with the certainty now in their minds. Abreaction (see page 244) does not necessarily require outside intervention; indeed, this may be the power of prayer, a self-analytical abreaction.

THE BEGGAR AT THE BEAUTIFUL GATE

The beggar who walked at the command of Peter and John (3:7) was probably an imposter who, being found out, had little alternative but to pretend that he was cured or lose his living. Insufficient details are given for any other diagnosis.

ANANIAS'S DEATH

Ananias had sold some land and, with the connivance of his wife, Sapphira, only gave part of the proceeds to the Apostles, while pretending that he was giving all the profit from the sale. When Peter confronted him with his deceit, he fell down dead (5:5). Sapphira, ignorant of what had happened to her husband, was asked by Peter to confirm the lower price for the land. She did so and was then told that her husband had died and was buried. Hearing this, she too fell down dead (5:10). It is no good pretending that Peter did not play a dirty trick on Sapphira. The obvious cause of the deaths (in the absence of clinical details) is ischaemic heart disease or coronary thrombosis. Two deaths one after the other are a coincidence though not impossible, but one has to consider whether the man and his wife fainted and were, in fact, buried alive. Quick burial was not unusual but clearly had its dangers.

FREE SPEECH

Gamaliel's plea for toleration (5:34) is notable. Once more the Jews are described as stiff-necked, this time by Stephen (7:51), and further as stultified in their minds. These comments, combined with a long speech, seem to have been the immediate cause of his being stoned to death (7:59).

PAUL'S DISSOCIATED STATE

Saul, of the tribe of Benjamin, later called Paul (13:9), consented to and witnessed the murder of Stephen and guarded the clothes of those who stoned him to death (7:58). Saul was 'still breathing threats and murder against the disciples of the Lord' (9:1) when he obtained a commission sometime between AD35 – 37 from the High Priest to go to Damascus to round up deviants and obtain their extradition as offenders against Jewish law. He found the burden of guilt of Stephen's murder more than his psyche could bear. His breakdown on the road to Damascus was signalled by a bright light. His anxiety expressed itself as a challenge: 'Saul, Saul, why do you persecute me?' (9:4). Inability to see was the analogue of the psychic trauma of Stephen's murder, an inability of the mind to withstand the pressures of what he knew was wrong. Saul asked: 'Who are you, Lord?' The reply was: 'I am Jesus, whom you are persecuting.' Saul's companions saw nothing (9:7). Commenting on this incident, Coggan[2] chose to call the psychological processes an enquiry, a revelation and a` command. Paul's later account of the incident (I

Corinthians 15:5, Galatians 1:16) is important in relation to the Apostles' perception of Jesus when he is recorded as appearing in the forty days after the Crucifixion. Paul uses the Greek *ōphthē* to describe all Jesus's post-Crucifixion appearances (see page 235) although there was no possibility of a physical appearance on the road to Damascus.

In Damascus, Ananias, who was a disciple, explained his visit to Saul, which could have been construed as interference even if it was meant to help, by saying that Jesus had sent him. Undoubtedly Ananias knew of Saul's presence in Damascus and the reason for it. Saul had failed to rationalise his fear in three days of self-examination (9:9), but the laying on of hands by Ananias (9:17) provoked the discharge of emotional tension requisite for his recovery. Saul's secondary gain was a change in his mission in life without loss of face. The adventure of being let down in a basket over the wall (9:25) to escape from the Jews no doubt raised his self-esteem with its sense of daring.

TABITHA AND DISSOCIATION

Hysteria should not be diagnosed because of the absence of physical symptoms or the lack of a reliable case history, but with Aeneas (9:34) and Tabitha (9:41) neither history nor clinical details are available. Aeneas who had been bedridden for eight years was suffering from conversion hysteria (paralysis) and Tabitha who is said to have died, from extreme dissociation. Tabitha may have felt emotionally that her good works were not properly appreciated. Not to be loved was intolerable – what has one to live for?

PSYCHOLOGICAL AND NEUROLOGICAL PROCESSES

In the evolution of men and animals, there came a time when individuals became aware of their thoughts (even if these were devoted to the satisfaction of needs), were able to remember these thoughts and to associate causality. They became conscious beings. As evolutionary time went on, language (not necessarily verbal) and art developed as means of communication.

Irrefutable evidence exists that intellectual processes take place in the cerebral cortex and emotional processes in the thalamic or sub-thalamic part of the brain. The joke that the intellect exists to find reasons for one's prejudices (emotions) contains a grain of truth; without emotions life would be very dull.

Sigmund Freud[3] (1856–1939), while practising as a neurologist in Vienna, observed a female patient who in every session relived a long-forgotten incident in her early life. Freud proposed that the mind (psyche) has three elements: subconscious (unconscious), conscious (ego) and super-ego. Mental processes of which the conscious is unaware and which are not rational are constantly going on. The deepest layer of unconsciousness, the id, can be thought of as the font of psychic energy constantly presenting ideas to the ego. Some need to be censored by the super-ego before they can be accepted. If not accepted, they may be suppressed, to appear in a disguised form in dreams. Freud's scheme has been much criticised because of its emphasis on sexual and death instincts, but it is important to note that the super-ego is peculiar to the individual.

Carl Gustav Jung[4] (1875–1961) identified complexes in the unconscious processes that led him to propose the presence of a collective unconscious derived from primeval experiences. With Freud, man is a product of external influences. With Jung, man has a psychic life open to primeval forces of long ago. Jung went on to develop the idea of personality types e.g. introvert, extrovert, in modes of thinking.

The term hysteria was used by the Greeks in the mistaken belief that bizarre movements, or lack of movements, seen in young women were due to the uterus (Greek *hustera*) migrating through the body. In the Middle Ages, the term persisted but the unconscious nature of the force behind the symptoms was, in the climate of the times, ascribed to religious causes, particularly to possession by evil spirits. Pierre Marie Felix Janet[5] (1859–1947) developed the idea of dissociation of consciousness so that incompatible ideas did not occur together. Unfortunately this very useful concept was spoilt by his insistence that dissociation arose from sexual inadequacy. Conversion hysteria is the term applied where painful situations are avoided by developing physical signs, e.g. paralysis of a limb or loss of speech. Often, a secondary gain is sympathy or avoidance of loss of 'face'. Hysteria is rarely seen in Britain nowadays, partly because of changes in religious thought and also because better education allows self-understanding of symptoms. Hysterical symptoms tend to be of sudden onset, persistent and consistent and to resolve with remarkable speed.

Considering the Scriptures it is surprising that the Jews had so little insight into the workings of the mind. This may be due to the rigidity of Moses's theocracy. If everything, especially events with no obvious explanation, is the will of the Lord, there is not much point in enquiry.

Emotions arise when needs such as hunger and thirst are not met or when a desired goal is not achieved. Some emotions, such as fear and anger, evoke considerable psychic energy. Emotions are deeply rooted in culture. In most environments, most people resolve their fear or anxiety, but, if the psychic tension increases because of increasing stress, mental breakdown occurs. Relief requires discharge of emotion. Many people are able to do this by themselves, whether by thinking about the problem, a good night's sleep, having a good cry, self-analysis, sedation, the use of alcohol, talking to friends or by counselling, but in more severe cases formal intervention is required. This may take the form of psychoanalysis, or the therapeutic induction of fear (not necessarily the same as that which precipitated the breakdown) so that emotional discharge or abreaction may be secured.

Drug induced abreaction was developed by Sargant[6,7] for the treatment of battle neurosis, an example of extreme stress. While under light narcosis, the circumstances of the precipitatory fear were created in the patient's mind so that emotional exhaustion, and ultimately collapse, followed. On waking up, the patient's fear had gone and he felt well. The psycho-pathology was, though not known to Sargant at the time, identical to that found in Pavlov's conditioned dogs. Ivan Petrovich Pavlov[8] (1849–1936) was endeavouring to discover the physiological basis of thought. The well-known example of Pavlov's conditioned reflexes was the ringing of a bell when a meal was served to dogs who showed normal salivation. When the reflex was established, the ringing of a bell alone resulted in salivation and, more importantly, in bewilderment and distress.

Many of Pavlov's experiments would not now be tolerated in Britain as being too cruel, but the biggest stress applied to the dogs happened fortuitously. In the Leningrad flood of 1924, the river Neva overflowed into the laboratory and the dogs survived by swimming to keep their noses in the pocket of air between the water and the ceilings of their cages. When the dogs were rescued, Pavlov described them as having undergone transmarginal stress, i.e. stress beyond the capacity of the brain to cope.

There were three distinguishable phases of increasingly abnormal behaviour. First, the equivalent phase when all stimuli, strong and weak, produced the same result; secondly, the paradoxical phase when weak stimuli produced greater responses than strong ones; and, thirdly, the ultra-paradoxical phase when positive conditioned patterns suddenly became negative and vice versa, e.g. the dog began to hate his master and fawn upon those whom he had previously shunned. Debilitating procedures, confinement, isolation, fatigue, starvation and also disease increase liability to emotional breakdown. Personal susceptibility varies widely.

For those who accept Pavlov's interpretation, a physiological basis for differing psychological responses is available, the more so as Pavlov later speculated that small areas of the brain might be inhibited while other small areas might be excited and that these areas might change from one to the other very quickly.

Pavlov distinguished four types of inherited temperament in his dogs: calm imperturbable, lively, weak inhibitory and strong excitatory (incidentally corresponding to the humours of Aristotle, 384–322 BC). Whatever their temperament, all the dogs could be made to become inhibited, but the weak inhibitory and strong excitatory types did so with lower levels of stress. Precise human parallels exist.

RELIGION AND SEX

This may be a convenient point to ask why the Bible (both Old and New Testaments) has such a constantly recurring sexual overlay. John Wesley, by a lucky accident, discovered that men and women whose squalid daily lot echoed their fear of future hell-fire might be brought to a state of emotional (and often physical) collapse by preaching the terrible consequences of sin.[6,7]

Whether emotional exhaustion is produced by extreme fatigue (as in battle or questioning by the KGB), by the fear of certain and eternal damnation after death (John Wesley), by fasting, by the beat of drums and dancing to saturate the brain (voodooism and rock gospel), by sexual excitement (orgasm), the basis of sudden conversion exists in the calm that follows in which the mind will accept new ideas and reject the old (see Figure 8).

A person becomes open to the uncritical adoption of thought and behaviour patterns which would normally not have been acceptable either emotionally or intellectually. This state of heightened susceptibility after the release of

Figure 8. The Ecstasy of St. Teresa (Bernini) shows extreme
emotional collapse (see page 244)

emotional tension is one of the hallmarks of religious revivalist meetings from those of John Wesley in the eighteenth century, through those of Billy Graham in this century to the rock gospel of today. The essential requirement, whether induced by revivalist preachers, the Beatles, sexual orgasm, floods in Leningrad, terrors of war, interrogation techniques or voodooism, is to produce emotional collapse which is replaced by certainty and often the acceptance of previously unacceptable thoughts. This may be lifelong or, as John Wesley found, need reinforcing by periodic follow-up.

There are two corollaries: first, sex and religion are linked and sects puritanically queasy about sex are unlikely to prosper, and, secondly, a Protestantism which depends solely on appeal to the intellect (and rejects all emotional appeal) will not succeed.

DAYDREAMS

Cornelius, a Roman centurion based at Caesarea, had a 'vision' of an angel who told him to send for Peter who was then at Joppa (10:1). The 'vision' of Cornelius and the 'dream' of Peter (10:9) are interesting examples of daydreaming and a dissociated state. A daydream really consists of drowsy thinking in which delusory perceptions have sway, especially if sensory stimuli are reduced (as in a quiet environment) and attention is concentrated on one objective. A daydream may proceed to a dissociated state. When dissociated states are induced, deprivation of food is used as an additional means of raising susceptibility but Simon Peter's complaint of hunger is doubtfully of this degree. Contents of dreams and daydreams are influenced by real life, in Cornelius's case the knowledge that Peter was at Joppa. Quite possibly the angel who told him was a man or a soldier. What influenced Peter's dream (incidentally God affirmed that no food is unclean) is hard to decide, but he may have had some idea that Cornelius was a suitable subject for conversion.

SUPERSTITIOUS FEAR

According to Josephus,[9] Herod Agrippa was seized with sudden and severe abdominal pain when he saw a white owl sitting on the ropes of the procuratorial canopy. The Jews ascribed this incident to the fact that, after his oration to them, Herod accepted the attribution of divinity when hailed as a god by a deputation from Tyre and Sidon. He died, according to Josephus, four days later, 'eaten by worms' (12:23). Gwilt[10] suggests that death was due to anaphylaxis consequent upon the rupture of a hydatid cyst. Hydatid cysts have a thick wall further strengthened by encapsulation by the host; they are unlikely to burst. Death from anaphylaxis would be almost immediate.

Herod had been angry with the people of Tyre and Sidon. The deputation seems to have entered his presence by a trick and a white owl was a bird of ill omen. The sudden and severe pain of massive coronary ischaemia may be present in the abdomen; being eaten by worms would be explained by the passage of segments of the beef tapeworm (*Taenia saginata*) which may grow to 30 feet (9 m) or more in length in the faeces. The segments are seen easily, being about half an inch (1 – 2 cm) across. Such an infestation would have been common.

CONVERSION HYSTERIA

Paul's scathing denunciation of Elymas, a magician, created such fear in Elymas's mind that he avoided the challenge by a conversion hysteria (blindness) or the pretence of it which lasted for a time (13:11).

THE CRIPPLE AT LYSTRA

The man at Lystra (14:8) had been crippled from birth (presumably with disabled feet) and had never walked. Club feet (of which the commonest is *talipes equinus-varus*) seem most likely (see page 128). Such patients can walk or hobble (even if painfully). A comfortable living, or the absence of a sufficiently strong motivation until Paul's command, seems a probable explanation, but details are too sketchy to be dogmatic.

STONING OF PAUL

In the story of Stephen (7:60), it is recorded that he knelt (which implies some degree of compliance even if this was unwilling). Paul's stoning seems to have been a shemozzle, not the judicial stoning of Jewish law. He was lucky to have been knocked unconscious early in the proceedings (14:19), but one can but hope, that before he was, he remembered Stephen.

GENTILES AND CIRCUMCISION

A conference of the Apostles and the elders of the Church was held at Jerusalem in AD 49 to decide whether converts to Christianity should be circumcised, i.e. should they receive the physical sign of a Jew, before being baptised. (Even now male domination persists in spite of the women friends of Jesus and the women 'fellow workers' of Paul (see page 256). An account of this conference is given in Chapter 15:1 – 20 and a more abrasive account by Paul in Galatians 2:1 – 10. The arguments against compulsory circumcision were put by Paul and Barnabas with some support from Peter. Eventually James pronounced that Gentile converts need not be circumcised but that they should observe certain precepts of the Mosaic law. Thanks to Paul's advocacy the decision of the conference marks a turning-point in the development of the Church, for it opened the way to the establishment of a universal Church, not one that could be regarded as a reform movement within Judaism.

THE SLAVE-GIRL

The slave-girl who called out as she followed Paul (16:18) may have been simple minded and may have been infatuated, but there seems no reason to believe that she had an evil spirit in her. Paul did no more than tell her to stop pestering him.

EUTYCHUS

At Troas, Paul talked to the people in a room, lit by many torches, on the third floor of a house. Paul 'prolonged his speech until midnight' and Eutychus, a young man sitting in the window listening, went to sleep and fell out of the window (20:9). This is perhaps the first example of sleep being induced by a long sermon, though probably the late hour, the crowd and the hot atmosphere produced by the torches added to Eutychus's drowsiness. Even if houses were lower than they are today, he was lucky to be only stunned. The Jews must have seen a lot of deaths; perhaps the uncleanness of corpses prevented them from distinguishing between death and unconsciousness. Paul, being released from the Mosaic code, 'embraced' Eutychus.

PAUL'S SHIPWRECK

Paul escaped the worst rigours of his compulsory journey to Rome by being a Roman citizen. His shipwreck in Malta seems to have brought good fortune, including no ill effects from a bite by a viper or adder (*Vipera aspis*, now extinct in Malta) (28:3). The snake's emergence from a bundle of sticks is in keeping with its habits (see page 166).

Publius's father (28:8) was suffering from dysentery. Probably in this context the term 'dysentery' is applied (and correctly so) to diarrhoea of bacterial origin. This may be very serious and even fatal in infants and old people; much depends on what bacteria is causative. Most cases described as diarrhoea recover with or without the laying on of hands. It is to be devoutly hoped that Paul washed his hands afterwards.

References

1. Smith G.A. *The Historical Geography of the Holy Land.* London: Collins (Fontana Library of Theology), 1966.
2. Coggan D. *Paul: Portrait of a Revolutionary.* London: Hodder & Stoughton, 1984.
3. Freud S. *The Interpretation of Dreams.* London: Allen & Unwin, 1922.
4. Jung C.G. *Psychological Types.* London: Routledge & Kegan Paul, 1953.
5. Janet P.M.F. *The Major Symptoms of Hysteria.* New York: Macmillan, 1907.
6. Sargant W. *Battle for the Mind: A Physiology of Conversion and Brainwashing.* London: Heinemann, 1957.
7. Sargant W. *The Mind Possessed.* London: Heinemann, 1973.
8. Pavlov I.P. Lectures on Conditioned Reflexes. : *Conditioned Reflexes and Psychiatry,* trans. Horsley Grant W. London: Laurence & Wishart, 1941.
9. Perowne S. *The Political Background of the New Testament.* London: Hodder & Stoughton, 1965.
10. Gwilt J.R. Biblical ills and remedies. *Journal of the Royal Society of Medicine.* 1986, **79**: 738.

23

THE EPISTLES

The Epistles are deficient in incidents requiring medical comment. In those written by Paul (the ascription of Colossians and Ephesians to him is now questionable and there is general agreement that the epistles to Timothy and Titus are by another author) the main interest is the character of Paul himself.

THE CHARACTER OF PAUL

A Jew fluent in Greek and a Roman citizen, Paul (originally called Saul) was steeped in Jewish culture. He studied under Rabbi Gamaliel (Acts 22:3), which may account for on occasion, his legalistic outlook (Romans 7:7). Paul wrote some of the most magnificent language, both in the original Greek and, thanks to the committee appointed by King James I, when translated into English as the Authorised Version of the Bible (1611). An outstanding example is I Corinthians 13:1 – 13 which Paul wrote between AD 53 – 54. Alas, the Revised Standard Version changes 'charity' to 'love'; the latter includes delight in the presence of the beloved, since the advent of television this has sexual innuendo and the former is more expressive of actions such as giving to the third world. Paul's mental bias may have been subjective,[1] when subject and object tend to merge. Certainly he was active both physically and mentally. His make-up may have mirrored Romans 6:15, which is a prescription for neurotic behaviour.

DISSOCIATED STATE

Paul guarded the clothes of those who stoned Stephen to death (Acts 7:58). At the time he was zealous in rounding up deviants from the Jewish faith for subsequent prosecution. There is no record that he felt depressed or anxious about his actions, either immediately or subsequently. However, on the road to Damascus, Paul underwent an hysterical fugue. His mind was no longer able to cope with the guilt and anxiety arising from the enormity of his crime, his consent to Stephen's death (Acts 8:1).

Certainly Paul was obsessive before his breakdown on the road to Damascus; he prosecuted deviants relentlessly. After recovering his rationality he showed even greater vigour in pursuing his new-found certainty.

WOMEN

Traditionally, Paul did not like women, though he was generous in the recognition of those he described as 'fellow workers' in the apostolate. A great many women occupy this place in Paul's entourage, for example, Euodia and Syntyche (Philippians 4:2), Phoebe, Prisca and Mary (Romans 16:1, 3, 6). This was something wholly alien to Judaism. The importance of women in Paul's missionary work has been overshadowed by his comments on the place of women in public worship. A woman who prays or prophesies must be veiled; if she has her head uncovered it is as disgraceful as if her head were shaven (I Corinthians 11:5). Women were made for men (I Corinthians 11:9), an attitude which is reminiscent of the behaviour of men in Genesis and the subordination of women. In Paul a strong libido (very likely in a man of his vigorous activity) combined with fear or abhorrence of sex derived from his upbringing. His remarks (I Corinthians 7:7, 11:9, 14:34) suggest that he feared temptation by a woman. All this was emotional; intellectually Paul realises that all men·and women are equal in Christ (Galatians 3:28).

WINE FOR STOMACH'S SAKE

Water, in spite of its importance, would be a dangerous drink. The author of the epistles to Timothy advocates a little wine for the stomach's sake (I Timothy 5:23). Alcohol depresses the brain (and other organs) as Noah found out (see page 14). Any comfortable feeling noticed by Timothy would be due to esters and aldehydes dervied from the grape during fermentation. The sense of sociability arising from wine depends on its taste and the fact that appreciation of personal failings and of the world is diminished.

THORN IN THE FLESH

Paul writes: 'a thorn was given me in the flesh' (II Corinthians 12:7). He regarded this as being given to prevent him from becoming too elated at the revelation of the Lord manifested to him (II Corinthians 12:1). Many suggestions, including malaria, have been made as to the nature of this recurrent affliction (II Corinthians 12:8ff.). Paul was physically active and mentally alert. About 5 per cent of such persons suffer from migraine, a recurrent but unpredictable attack of headache of varying severity, occasionally sufficient to cause incapacity, especially if accompanied by vomiting and visual disturbances, including flashes of light, which later may be followed by partial and temporary loss of sight. Migraine does not account for Paul's experience on the road to Damascus as it is not accompanied by behavioural changes. An alternative but unlikely diagnosis might be trigeminal neuralgia, but recurrent attacks of this would preclude Paul's activity because of crippling pain.

Whatever Paul's failings may have been, he was a man of great energy and stamina not only because of the hardships of his journeys but because of his survival from great adversities (II Corinthians 6:4, 11:23). He was the most intelligent and the best educated of the Apostles.

References

1. Jung C.G. *Psychological Types*. London: Routledge & Kegan Paul, 1953.

24

REVELATION

There is no consensus about the identity of the author of Revelation, whether he was John the Apostle, John the Elder or a pseudonymous John.

The vivid visual imagery displayed borders on the psychotic. Persistence of such imagery, that is, mental perceptions not derived immediately from sense organs, into adult life, is unusual. Verbal symbols become the means of communication. Ezekiel's phantasies were similar (see page 179). In general, incidents display the horrors awaiting man on earth followed by the wonders of the life to come in the presence of God and his angels. The author is fascinated with the figure seven. The only medical significance is the character of the author.

GLOSSARY

Abreaction	A working through of emotion (see page 244).
Achondroplasia	Premature ossification of cartilage, apparently of hereditary origin, leading to dwarfing and deformity.
Acromegaly	Acromegaly and gigantism both result from the increased secretion of growth hormone by the pituitary gland. If the increased secretion occurs before the fusion of the epiphyses, gigantism results. There is increasing stature, particularly noticeable in the height. Gigantism is usually associated with diffuse hyperplasia but in acromegaly a non-malignant tumour of the pituitary gland, an adenoma, is usually present. The adenoma may press on the optic chiasma, where the optic nerves from the eye join and cross, located immediately behind the pituitary gland so that blindness in different parts of the optic field may result.
Anaerobic	Capable of growth in the absence of oxygen.
Anaphylaxis	An acute, often explosive, reaction when a sensitised person receives the same antigen again.
Balinitis	Inflammation of the glans penis.

Crohn's disease   A granulomatous reaction of unknown origin affecting all parts of the gut.

Desquamation   The outer layer of the skin, the epidermis, normally sheds cells. Usually these are not noticeable, but if excessive may become visible. A simple example of this is dandruff.

Day precipitate dream   A dream which, according to popular legend, foretells the future.

Epiphyses   The cartilaginous ends of bones, particularly of long bones, which form a joint. Epiphyses fuse with bones at varying times of life, mostly at puberty.

Gaussian curve   A statistical curve showing the distribution of the population characteristic being studied. e.g. height.

Gigantism   See acromegaly.

Goitre   An enlargement of the thyroid gland. In hyperthyroidism the goitre is small and associated with excitability, rapid pulse rate, sweating and aversion to heat. Severe cases may have bulging eyes (exophthalmia). Hypothyroidism (in which the swelling is often easily visible) is associated with slow responses, thickened and cold skin and in severe cases mental retardation (cretinism).

Granuloma   A response by the tissues to slow acting bacilli or foreign bodies present over a long period. The response is characterised by the presence of giant cells (cells with more than one nucleus). Often a mass forms which in the centre undergoes necrosis (death of cells). A typical example is tuberculosis.

Growth hormones   See acromegaly.

Heat exhaustion   Caused by the inadequate replacement of salt lost through sweating.

Hemianopsia	Blindness on one side of the visual field.
Hyperthyroidism	See goitre.
Hypothyroidism	See goitre.
Hysteria	A short but fully adequate definition of hysteria is difficult. It must not be confused with histrionic behaviour or malingering. Hysteria is failure of synthesis of the personality so that conflict between incompatible emotions is avoided. The essential feature is a breakdown of the central nervous integration. In a trance the subject persists in his daily activities but cannot account for them, in a fugue there is wandering and loss of memory. Other manifestations are stupor, excitement to avoid conflict; clinical symptoms such as blindness, loss of voice, deafness and paralysis of limbs may develop. In Britain, hysteria is now uncommon; in other cultures and religious climates hysteria may be more 'acceptable'. The experimental induction of hysteria in dogs and the relation of this to religious conversion is discussed on page 245.
Ischaemia or Infarction	Reduction or obstruction of the blood supply to an organ, whether by narrowing of the arteries, thrombosis, (clotting of the blood in an artery) or embolus (a clot travelling in the blood stream).
Lead encephalopathy	Disordered function of the brain due to the ingestion of lead salts; occasionally may be manifest as fits.
Malar flush	Flushing of the skin over the cheek (malar) bone; may be a sign of back pressure in the venous system such as occurs in deformity of the mitral valve of the heart consequent upon earlier rheumatic fever.
Menorrhaghia	Abnormally heavy menstrual discharge.
Metrorrhaghia	Abnormal bleeding from the uterus.

Neurofibroma	A fibrous tumour arising from the sheath of nerves; if the auditory nerve is affected, deafness may result. Solitary tumours are of no great significance but occasionally, as in von Recklinghausen's disease, multiple tumours under the skin cause a marked disfigurement.
Oedema	Accumulation of fluid in the spaces between cells.
Optic chiasma	See acromegaly.
Osteoporosis	A disease of unknown origin in which the bone marrow is reduced. There are many causes, some of glandular origin but it is especially common in post menopausal women. Bones become brittle and fracture easily.
Propitus	Person, not a patient, who is the subject of study.
Resection	Removal of part or whole of an organ (e.g. lung or bone).
Seborrhoeic dermatitis	See Desquamation.
Silicosis	Fibrosis of the lung due to the presence of particles of silica.
Vesico-vaginal fistula	A pathological communication between the bladder and vagina.
Volaemic shock	Shock due to diminution of the volume of blood.

BIBLICAL INDEX

With the exception of the Gospels and the Epistles biblical references are only given where they are not from the chapter concerned.

GENERAL INDEX